# THE INTERNSHIP HANDBOOK

A Guide for Students in
the Health Professions

*First Edition*

## Kimberly L. McVicar and Julie Ward

Ferris State University

SAN DIEGO

Bassim Hamadeh, CEO and Publisher
Jennifer Codner, Senior Field Acquisitions Editor
Susana Christie, Senior Developmental Editor
Michelle Piehl, Senior Project Editor
Abbey Hastings, Production Editor
Emely Villavicencio, Senior Graphic Designer
Trey Soto, Licensing Specialist
Natalie Piccotti, Director of Marketing
Kassie Graves, Senior Vice President of Editorial
Jamie Giganti, Director of Academic Publishing

Cover image: Copyright © 2016 iStockphoto LP/ktasimarr.

Printed in the United States of America.

3970 Sorrento Valley Blvd., Ste. 500, San Diego, CA 92121

# Contents

# Introduction

Congratulations! If you are anticipating an internship experience, you have probably reached a significant milestone in your academic career. Experiential learning allows students to continue learning by working with experts in their field of study. It provides a unique opportunity for students to observe; be observed; apply the skills they learned in the didactic portion of their academic journey; acquire practical, professional experience; gain insight about where they see themselves working in the future; and network. Concurrently, internships afford employers the means of recruiting new talent and gaining fresh perspectives (Tyler, 2012).

The National Association of Colleges and Employers (NACE) suggests internship handbooks addressing topics such as commonly asked questions are a best practice in the field (NACE, 2020). Therefore, the purpose of this handbook is to provide a concise reference that helps students in health professions effectively transition from academic coursework to workplace life beyond the classroom. To achieve this goal, the authors have compiled a collection of best practices and resources surrounding internships, field placements, and clinical experiences—from beginning (evaluating sites) to end (seeking a job)—and presented them here enhanced by current literature and a wealth of feedback from students, faculty, and healthcare preceptors. Chapter 1 addresses the basics of getting started, beginning with selecting an internship site. Chapter 2 reviews legal and ethical issues surrounding the internship, such as policies and confidentiality. Chapter 3 offers practical tips on how to perfect your résumé and cover letter and ace your interviews. Chapters 4 and 5 review professionalism basics such as social media presence, time management, and soft skills. Chapter 6 reinforces the importance of diversity and inclusion in the workplace and beyond. Chapter 7 reveals tips and resources to facilitate successful transition from the internship to the workplace. In chapter 8, the authors conclude by sharing real stories of six interns from their academic institution for student consideration. Handbook chapters feature the following format:

- Brief overview
- Concise content delivery, including succinct, bulleted lists
- Quick reminders
- Journal prompts designed for organizing thoughts, expanding thinking and creativity, and enhancing reflection.

Students will be accountable to at least two people (other than themselves) during their internship experience: one at the academic institution and one at the internship site. Although titles may vary, the authors will clarify terminology for such individuals for the purpose of this handbook: faculty coordinator will refer to faculty from the student's academic institution, and site coordinator will refer to the individual who directly oversees the student's work within the healthcare facility.

Interns are advised to focus on the internship with as much passion and persistence as they would a new employment opportunity. You are likely paying for credits, so embrace a learn-all-you-can mindset. Be cognizant of the fact that this very important investment in yourself could lead to the job offers you have been working toward! A 2019 student survey conducted by NACE revealed that graduating college seniors who had completed an internship experience enjoyed a higher average number of job offers than students who did not complete an internship (NACE, 2019).

# References

National Association of Colleges and Employers (NACE). (2019). *Job offers for class of 2019 grads impacted by internship experience*. https://www.naceweb.org/job-market/trends-and-predictions/job-offers-for-class-of-2019-grads-impacted-by-internship-experience/

National Association of Colleges and Employers (NACE). (2020). *15 best practices for internship programs*. https://www.naceweb.org/talent-acquisition/internships/15-best-practices-for-internship-programs/

Tyler, K. (2012). Must-have: An HR internship. *HR Magazine, 57*(5), 31–34, 36, 38. https://www.shrm.org/hr-today/news/hr-magazine/pages/0512tyler.aspx

# 1

# GETTING STARTED

## Overview

A successful intern is an informed, prepared, and empowered one. Chapter 1 is designed to provide potential interns with information about navigating the process of securing an internship and introduce the initial experiential learning concepts students should consider. These include important contacts, site selection, and typical health-care site requirements, such as immunization records and background checks. Understanding the logistical concepts of an internship can help ensure a smooth process free of misunderstandings and unnecessary delays.

## The Role of the Intern

Interns must be prepared to seek new opportunities and learn new things while also being accountable to the knowledge gained during didactic experiences. Successful navigation of the inherent ambiguities of an internship in healthcare requires that the student be cognizant of the simultaneous expectations of their academic institution and healthcare organization. In doing so, the intern may occasionally feel confused or overwhelmed. This is normal. Brian Baird (2008) suggests potential role ambiguity by the intern can be minimized by adherence to two simple principles: The intern should be honest with oneself and others, and the intern should always exert his or her best effort. Remember to ask questions and seek clarification if you do not understand what expectations you are trying to fulfill. In addition, be sure to welcome new opportunities, embrace challenges, remain enthusiastic, and enjoy yourself!

The intern should be mindful that site coordinators have many responsibilities and may, therefore, expect the intern to work independently. That said, you should always seek clarification as needed; do not wait until an unnecessary amount of time has lapsed. Problems cannot be solved if nobody knows they exist (Covey, 1999). Be sure to ask your site coordinator how he or she would like you to approach him or her with questions; for example, understand if you should seek him or her out as questions arise, wait until the end of each workday, or schedule specific meeting times. Remember, faculty coordinators should also be available to intervene and answer questions as necessary.

## Selecting a Site

If your academic program allows you to select your own internship site, there are several factors to consider. Literature contends that word of mouth is an effective way of evaluating and comparing internship opportunities (Kelly, 2012; Baird, 2008). Students are encouraged to seek advice and historical perspectives about potential internship sites from faculty coordinators and previous student interns. While such advice can prove invaluable, the student must also keep in mind the personal nature of site selection.

Aside from networking with faculty and program graduates, students must also consider site reputation, mission, vision, and values to assess overall fit. Location, flexible scheduling, and future employment opportunities are also important to many students who balance busy lives. Much of this information will be easily accessible from organizational websites. Be sure to aspire to sites that will offer you substantive, challenging tasks. Lastly, most students want to know if paid internships are available to them. A 2011 study conducted by Intern Bridge revealed that health science majors report more unpaid than paid internships (Gardner, 2011). All elements considered, you should strive to secure an internship that is engaging, inclusive, and appropriately aligned with your professional goals. If you have not consciously reflected on your professional goals recently, now is the time! The values, vision, and mission template in Appendix B can be used as a starting point. Some students elect to intern where they wish to seek future employment. In these cases, consider the internship a form of working interview.

If your academic institution chooses your internship site for you, realize that the opportunity may not be in or near your hometown. In such cases, securing and paying for housing may be necessary. Students should understand these dynamics as early in the curriculum as possible so costs can be anticipated and planned for accordingly.

If your academic institution allows international internships, understand it will likely take longer to establish affiliation agreements with such organizations outside your home country. If you are interested in completing an internship outside the United States, give your faculty coordinator adequate advanced notice. Some universities may not allow internships outside of the United States.

Given the number of variables to keep in mind, it may be wise to create a short internship action plan. Items to consider may include:

- Here are the things I would like to learn during my internship experience (list as many as possible):

- Here are the organizational attributes I value most (such as flexible scheduling):

- Here is a reminder of the requirements of my academic institution (e.g., written projects. The authors' Health Care Systems Administration program requires students to complete projects in areas such as managerial skills, finance, human resources, process improvement, privacy, data security and information systems, materials management, and reimbursement methods, in addition to completing a minimum number of internship hours. Administrative projects are also required. Administrative projects are generally conceptualized by the student and their Site Coordinator, and have included projects such as updating departmental policies and procedures, analyzing patient data to make recommendations, project planning, and utilizing A3 worksheets to problem solve and/or improve quality):

- Here is a reminder of the requirements of my internship site (once selected):

- Here is a list of things I believe I will need to maximize my internship experience and grade (list may include personal attributes such as patience):

# Virtual and Alternate Internships

The coronavirus pandemic has led to rapid conceptualization and implementation of virtual experiential learning opportunities (Slanetz, Parikh, Chapman, & Motuzas, 2020). The uncertainties surrounding the future of virtual internships in healthcare remain vast. Critics have expressed concern that students, particularly those with little or no healthcare experience, could be missing out on vital opportunities to enhance key soft skills such as understanding professional cultures and networking (NACE, 2020). However, the topic warrants mention here as distance learning modalities offer distinct benefits, such as flexibility and the ability to reduce geographical barriers. Universities, including the authors' own, have devised alternate internship learning activities that leverage resources such as webinars and case study scenarios (AUPHA, 2016). Human resource professionals have begun to establish best practices related to remote employees and remote career readiness. For example, Society for Human Resource Management (SHRM) blogger Brett Farmiloe (2020) emphasizes the use of videos that personally welcome new employees and introduce organizational procedures during a virtual onboarding process. Students are advised to consult their faculty coordinators about the feasibility of a virtual internship.

# Immunizations

While specific immunization requirements will vary by academic institution, program, and clinical site, there are a few things the student can do to prepare for immunization requirements. The Centers for Disease Control and Prevention's Advisory Committee on Immunization Practices (ACIP) recommends that healthcare personnel, including students, receive vaccines for measles, mumps, rubella, hepatitis B, varicella, influenza, and pertussis (Shefer et al., 2011). Students should be prepared to provide proof of immunity to the above conditions or proof of the recommended number of vaccine injections. Tuberculosis (TB) testing may also be required. The TB test can be a time-sensitive, two-step process; be sure to understand the process in advance. Delays in the process could defer your start date. If you are inclined to develop an internship budget, understand you may be responsible for the cost of immunizations. Academic institutions or individual departments or programs may provide immunization tracking assistance to students via compliance companies and collaborative platforms such as CastleBranch (CastleBranch, 2020) and ACEMAPP (Acemapp, 2021).

# Background Checks and Drug Testing

Healthcare organizations may also require interns to undergo background checks and/or drug testing. Sound background check and drug-testing programs can help employers ensure a safe workplace environment. Compliance companies such as CastleBranch can also assist with these requirements. Like immunizations, students may be responsible for these costs. Again, as a student, you should be familiar with your university's or program's resources.

Background checks are regulated by federal and state laws. If a healthcare organization wishes to perform a background check on an intern, it should obtain the intern's written consent (EEOC, 2014). Drug testing policy has been shaped by federal, state, and civil rights legislation (SAMHSA, 2020); most states allow preemployment drug screens (Nagele-Piazza, 2020). As part of their internship preparation, students should be cognizant of the laws applicable within their states. If students anticipate any adverse findings on either the background check or drug test, they should discuss these concerns with their faculty coordinator as soon as possible.

## GETTING STARTED REMINDERS

- Evaluate multiple site opportunities to identify best fit.
- Have your immunization records in order.
- Anticipate requests for a background check and/or drug screen.
- Consider formulating an internship action plan.
- Don't be afraid to ask questions!

## EXERCISE/JOURNAL PROMPT: SITE SELECTION

After considering the action plan items listed in this chapter, identify three organizations with whom you would be interested in pursuing an internship. Be sure to consider your program requirements (e.g., are you permitted to pursue out-of-state and international opportunities). This may require research into your respective organization picks as well (e.g., do they offer the type of internship you are seeking). Bonus exercise: try to rank these organizations (1–3) in terms of best fit for you. Remember to consider potential budget constraints. Organize your thoughts on the Chapter 1 Journal Page provided.

# Chapter 1 Journal Page

# References

Acemapp. (2021). *About Us*. https://acemapp.org/c/about-us

Association of University Programs in Health Administration (AUPHA). (2016). *COVID-19 resources*. https://www.aupha.org/faculty/covid19

Baird, B. N. (2008). *The internship, practicum, and field placement handbook: A guide for the helping professions* (5th ed.). Upper Saddle River, NeJ: Pearson/Prentice Hall.

CastleBranch. (2020). *Why CastleBranch?* https://discover.castlebranch.com/why-castlebranch/

Covey, S. R. (1999). *Living the 7 habits: The courage to change*. New York, NY: Fireside.

Farmiloe, B. (2020). *10 virtual onboarding tips for remote employees*. Society for Human Resource Management Blog. https://blog.shrm.org/blog/10-virtual-onboarding-tips-for-remote-employees?utm_source=all&utm_medium=social&utm_campaign=communications~comms_general~10_virtual_onboarding_tips_for_remote_employees

Gardner, P. (2011). *The debate over unpaid college internships*. Intern Bridge. http://citeseerx.ist.psu.edu/viewdoc/download?doi=10.1.1.372.1710&rep=rep1&type=pdf

Kelly, W. (2012). Academic advice for students about internship selection. *Journal of the Alabama Academy of Science, 83*(1), 37+.

Nagele-Piazza, L. (2020). *Workplace drug testing: Weighing the pros and cons*. Society for Human Resource Management. Retrieved from https://www.shrm.org/resourcesandtools/legal-and-compliance/state-and-local-updates/pages/the-pros-and-cons-of-workplace-drug-testing.aspx

National Association of Colleges and Employers (NACE). (2020). *Challenges to account for with virtual internships*. https://www.naceweb.org/talent-acquisition/internships/challenges-to-account-for-with-virtual-internships/

Shefer, A., Atkinson, W., Friedman, C., Kuhar, D. T., Mootrey, G., Bialek, S. R., Cohn, A., Fiore, A., Grohskopf, L., Liang, J. L., Lorick, S. A., Marin, M., Mintz, E., Murphy, T. V., Newton, A., Fiebelkorn, A. P., Seward, J., & Wallace, G. (2011). *Immunization of health-care personnel: Recommendations of the Advisory Committee on Immunization Practices (ACIP)*. Centers for Disease Control and Prevention. https://www.cdc.gov/mmwr/preview/mmwrhtml/rr6007a1.htm

Slanetz, P. J., Parikh, U., Chapman, T., & Motuzas, C. L. (2020). Corona-virus disease 2019 (COVID-19) and radiology education—strategies for survival. *Journal of the American College of Radiology: JACR, 17*(6), 743–745. https://doi.org/10.1016/j.jacr.2020.03.034

Substance Abuse and Mental Health Services Administration (SAMHSA). (2020). *Drug-free workplace programs.* https://www.samhsa.gov/workplace/workplace-programs

U.S. Equal Employment Opportunity Commission (EEOC). (2014). *Background checks: What employers need to know.* https://www.eeoc.gov/eeoc/publications/background_checks_employers.cfm

# 2

# LEGAL AND ETHICAL ISSUES

## Overview

Chapter two describes the legal and ethical issues interns should be aware of, such as affiliation agreements, policies, informed consent, confidentiality, liability, ethical documents, and removal from internship. It is essential for interns to understand that during their experiential learning opportunity, they must adhere to both their academic institution's and their internship site's rules, regulations, and policies. Failure to be informed of and comply with legal guidelines could lead to internship termination.

## Affiliation Agreements

Although students are involved to varying degrees in their development, it is important for them to be aware of the existence of affiliation or institutional agreements between academic institutions and internship sites. While these documents will vary in composition, literature suggests common elements include responsibilities and expectations of individual parties. Examples include, but are not limited to, begin and end dates, guidelines for conduct and disciplinary action, ethical issues, performance evaluation, confidentiality, liability and injury insurance (Baird & Mollen, 2018), criminal background checks, pre-clinical instruction for students, and maintenance of educational records. Given the inclusive nature of these documents, legal counsel from both organizations is often consulted. All negotiations should be settled prior to the intern's official internship start date. Students should understand that the affiliation agreement establishment process can be lengthy and should be completed as soon as possible to avoid delays in start date. Most affiliation agreements are not negotiated on a per-student basis; your academic institution will likely have existing agreements with healthcare organizations that cover specified groups of students. These documents are put into place as a form of protection from liability; therefore, the intern should be patient and supportive of the process.

## Policies

As mentioned previously, at this point in their education, interns become accountable to multiple parties. In terms of your academic institution, you will want to be aware of policies pertaining to work schedule. University academic calendars and hospital work schedules can differ. As an intern, you must understand your ability or inability to report to work if your faculty coordinator is on a holiday break, for example. Similarly, it is essential to understand policies related to absences and making up missed days. Employers are not likely to hire someone who has persistent attendance and/or tardiness issues, so be sure this is not an issue during your internship. Lastly, it is important to understand how your ultimate internship performance will be evaluated or graded. For example, are you responsible for submitting formal written projects in addition to completing a required minimum number of hours? If so, are there formal rubrics you should consult? Interns will likely play a role in communicating university policies to clinical site coordinators.

Once accepted, the intern will also be accountable to the policies within the healthcare organization (clinical site). Violation of policies could result in termination of the internship. Orientations are considered an internship best practice (NACE, 2020), and most interns are expected to attend new-hire orientations as a requirement of the Joint Commission. Items you should pay particular attention to include, but are not limited to, confidentiality, safety, emergency codes, dress code, breaks, parking, and cell phone use. If you are given a computer during your internship, be mindful that the computer belongs to the organization. The organization may have the ability to generate usage reports indicating time spent on the device as well as sites visited.

Taking notes during orientation and other significant experiences throughout your internship is advised.

# Informed Consent

Informed consent is an ethical and patients' rights principle that requires healthcare providers to effectively inform patients of the nature, risks, benefits, and alternatives of treatments or procedures (AHRQ, 2019; Showalter, 2015). Patients have the right to understand the qualifications of their providers. If your internship experience includes performing procedures on or treating patients, your intern status should be disclosed. This is something you can practice. Know what you are going to say in advance so you can put your client/patient at ease. If you are under the supervision of another individual, disclose that as well, for added reassurance to the client/patient.

# Confidentiality

The Health Insurance Portability and Accountability Act of 1996 (HIPAA) requires regulations protecting the privacy and security of certain health information. Health information has been defined as "any information, whether oral or recorded in any form or medium, that—(A) is created or received by a health care provider, health plan, public health authority, employer, life insurer, school or university, or health care clearinghouse; and (B) relates to the past, present, or future physical or mental health or condition of an individual; or the past, present, or future payment for the provision of health care to an individual" (Showalter, 2015, p. 291). The U.S. Department of Health and Human Services (HHS) published the Privacy and Security Rules related to protected health information (PHI). The *Standards for Privacy of Individually Identifiable Health Information*, or Privacy Rule, establishes national standards for the protection of certain health information. The *Security Rule* establishes a national set of security standards for protecting certain health information that is maintained or transferred in electronic form. Interns have most likely learned about HIPAA and the significance of PHI in the didactic portion of their respective health programs. Interns are advised to adhere to regulations strictly during their clinical experiences; be vigilant about sharing PHI with colleagues and do not discuss patients or patient information with friends and family members outside the workplace. When discussing patients in the workplace, be certain to do so in private rather than public places such as the cafeteria, hallways, or elevators. Do not post about patients or patient information on your personal social media accounts. Projects submitted to faculty coordinators or shared with classmates during internship should be devoid of PHI.

Zabel (2016) suggests common HIPAA violations include: health records being mishandled, devices containing PHI getting lost or stolen, patient information being shared via text, patient photos being posted on social media, employees illegally accessing patient files, inadvertent disclosure of patient information during social or informal situations, and accessing patient information from home or personal devices. Interns are advised to understand their healthcare organizations' policies and procedures and to ask questions if anything is unclear. If you are concerned you have violated HIPAA, even inadvertently, report it immediately to both your faculty and site coordinators.

## Liability Insurance

It is important for students to understand the potential for liability claims in healthcare. Such claims may arise when a healthcare professional's conduct falls below a standard of care (Tipton, 2017). While the process may be complex and involve insurance brokers, human resource professionals, and legal counsel, you should know if you are covered during your internship experience and by whom (Scerbinski, 2010).

## Ethical Documents

Ethical documents, such as codes of conduct or codes of ethics, exist for all professions. The development and maintenance of such documents serve as a means of accountability. Students should consider engaging with some of the ethical documents that guide their respective professions. Site and faculty coordinators can assist with this. The American College of Healthcare Executives' (ACHE, 2020) code of conduct can be found at https://www.ache.org/about-ache/our-story/our-commitments/ethics/ache-code-of-ethics.

# Removal from Internship

It is important for academic programs to have policies for conflict resolution, corrective action, and potential termination of an intern from their clinical site. HIPAA violations may be cause for termination from internship. Commonly cited reasons for internship terminations include behavior that is considered inappropriate or harmful to clients, students, or others; illegal or immoral behavior; and behavior that defies personal or professional boundaries, such as dating a colleague, performing outside one's authority, and violations of social media policy (Kiser, 2016; Sweitzer & King, 2019). Other causes for removal include lack of respect for others, lack of productivity, and lack of adherence to policies. Do not let these discourage you; you're going to be great! Nonetheless, make sure you are informed about policies before you begin your internship experience.

> **LEGAL AND ETHICAL ISSUES REMINDERS**
>
> - Communicate your internship site intentions to your faculty coordinator so affiliation agreements can be verified/established as timely as possible.
>
> - Understand the guiding policies of internship from both your academic institution and your clinical site.
>
> - Review HIPAA regulations. If you question something on internship, be sure to ask your site coordinator for clarification.

## EXERCISE/JOURNAL PROMPT: PATIENT CONFIDENTIALITY

You are in the second week of your healthcare administration internship at a small, acute care hospital. You are spending the day with a coding specialist. While she is explaining the concept of establishing medical necessity, you recognize the name of the person whose medical record currently appears on her computer screen. The patient, in fact, is the mother of a good friend of yours.

Two days later, you run into your good friend at the grocery store. He lets you know his mother has been ill lately and doesn't like to discuss any of her medical details with her children. He then remembers you are interning at the local hospital and asks if by chance you know whether his mother has been seeking any medical care there.

How should you respond to your friend? How do you maintain appropriate patient confidentiality?

Organize your thoughts on the Chapter 2 Journal Page provided or discuss in small groups (or both). Try to write at least 100 words.

# Chapter 2 Journal Page

# References

Agency for Healthcare Research and Quality (AHRQ). (2019). *AHRQ's making informed consent an informed choice: Training modules for health care leaders and professionals.* https://www.ahrq.gov/professionals/systems/hospital/informedchoice/index.html

American College of Healthcare Executives (ACHE). (2020). *ACHE Code of Ethics.* https://www.ache.org/about-ache/our-story/our-commitments/ethics/ache-code-of-ethics.

Baird, B. N. (2008). *The internship, practicum, and field placement handbook: A guide for the helping professions* (5th ed.). Upper Saddle River: NJ: Pearson/Prentice Hall.

Baird, B. N., & Mollen, Debra. (2019). *The internship, practicum, and field placement handbook: A guide for the helping professions* (8th ed.). New York, NY: Taylor & Francis.

Kiser, P. M. (2016). *The Human services internship: Getting the most from your experience* (4th ed.). Boston, MA: Cengage Learning.

National Association of Colleges and Employers (NACE). (2020). *15 best practices for internship programs.* https://www.naceweb.org/talent-acquisition/internships/15-best-practices-for-internship-programs/

Scerbinski, J. (2010). College interns: An entrepreneurial response to a cost-conscious economy. *New England Journal of Entrepreneurship, 13*(1), 73–77. https://doi.org/10.1108/NEJE-13-01-2010-B006

Showalter, J. S. (2015). *The law of healthcare administration* (7th ed.). Chicago, IL: Health Administration Press.

Sweitzer, H. F., & King, M. A. (2019). *The successful internship: Personal, professional, and civic development in experiential learning.* Boston, MA: Cengage Learning.

Tipton, D. (2017). *Personal and professional growth for health care professionals.* Burlington, MA: Jones and Bartlett Learning.

U.S. Department of Health and Human Services (HHS). (2013). *Summary of the HIPAA Security Rule."* https://www.hhs.gov/hipaa/for-professionals/security/laws-regulations/index.html

Zabel, L. (2016). *10 common HIPAA violations and preventative measures to keep your practice in compliance. Becker's Health IT.* https://www.beckershospitalreview.com/healthcare-information-technology/10-common-hipaa-violations-and-preventative-measures-to-keep-your-practice-in-compliance.html

**3**

# RÉSUMÉS, COVER LETTERS, AND INTERVIEWS

## Overview

Chapter 3 covers résumés, cover letters, and interviews: items that provide healthcare organizations with first impressions of potential intern candidates. This chapter also touches on job applications. Students should approach these items with passion, professionalism, and preparedness, as there are no second chances to make first impressions. Informed, intentional résumé- and cover letter–writing and interview preparation can help students secure their desired internship and employment opportunities.

## Résumés and Cover Letters

Professional résumés and cover letters are essential to the internship-seeking (and job-seeking) process. They are often your means of making a first impression and communicating how you uniquely distinguish yourself from other candidates. An important thing to remember here is to do your research and know your resources. If you are preparing these documents for the first time, you can begin with a simple Microsoft Word, Google Docs, or equivalent template. Two common résumé formats include the chronological layout, which emphasizes a timeline of prior work history and experiences, and the functional organization, which devotes more page space to a candidate's specific skills. Hybrids of these formats also exist. Literature suggests that reviewers prefer chronological résumé formats for their organization, ease of understanding, and ability to link specific skill sets to respective employment positions (Smith & Berg, 2020).

Your academic institution may make résumé building resources available to you via writing centers or career centers; they may even offer résumé reviews. Use the resources afforded to you; they are designed to help you present yourself in a professional manner. Program faculty can likely offer assistance as well; they have been with you during your academic journey and can often help you articulate your positive attributes. Lastly, professional organizations for your respective careers may also offer useful resources.

The Society for Human Resource Management (Enelow & Kursmark, 2020) offers valuable résumé tips, which include: Begin with a distinctive career summary, share details about your places of employment, highlight achievements and skills, groom your résumé for automated systems, share what makes you unique, and write succinctly. Literature recommends that most résumés be limited to two pages (Yate, 2020). Effective career summaries should demonstrate the value and expertise an individual can bring to an organization. Enelow (2018) provides several examples of career summary formats; students are encouraged to review them and select a style that compliments their overall résumé design. While résumés summarize experiences, skills, and achievements, cover letters may address common items of interest to recruiters or hiring organizations, such as why an individual is interested in an organization, how the individual is uniquely qualified for the position, and why employment gaps exist on a résumé (this only applies to applicants who have employment gaps). Lyden (2009, p. 72) suggests a cover letter should "increase the curiosity of potential employers enough to motivate them to contact you."

The National Association of Colleges and Employers provides access to résumé rubrics that allow students to evaluate their document on education, experience, involvement, visual allure, organization, individuality, and spelling, grammar, and punctuation (NACE, 2020). The American College of Healthcare Executives (ACHE) offers personalized résumé reviews to members and nonmembers for a fee. Completed critiques include digital and audio suggestions as well as sample résumés for additional reference (ACHE, 2020a). The American Health Information Management Association (AHIMA) offers student member access to career preparation webinars addressing résumé building, interviewing, and networking (AHIMA, 2019). Professional web platforms such as CareerBuilder also offer résumé building and career development tools (CareerBuilder, 2019).

It is advisable to tailor résumés and cover letters to each specific internship (or job) opportunity and organization. Use respective intern postings to help with this. Key words from the essential qualifications portion of the intern posting should appear in your résumé and cover letter as applicable. This tip also applies to résumés and key words in job descriptions as you begin to seek employment. Focus on essential key words can help ensure that your résumé is not rejected by auto-mated résumé-scanning tools or applicant-tracking systems (ATSs) that utilize artificial intelligence (AI) (Enelow, 2020; Malvey & Sapp, 2020). Remember also to tailor your résumé to your specific status as a member of the workforce. For example, résumés will look a bit different for a student who is seeking his or her first job versus someone who is reentering the workforce after several years off to raise a family. Again, resources are available to assist with your individualized needs. As a good example, NACE offers best practices to veterans developing their résumés (Rosser, 2017). If your work experience is limited (which can be common for students), Makely, Austin, and Kester (2017) suggest you include academic accomplishments and extracurricular activities such as awards, sports, musical involvement, science fair entries, or participation in other school organizations. It is always important to include leadership roles you may have held, unique trainings you may have received, and community service and other volunteer opportu-nities you have participated in. Literature suggests students should include their grade point average (GPA) (Lyden, 2009) and not include their photo (Malvey & Sapp, 2020) on their healthcare résumés.

Three final notes on résumé writing: while the objective is to sell yourself, be advised not to overstate your qualifications. Research sug-gests that as many as 70% of applicants exaggerate their employment qualifications (Makely, Badasch, & Chesebro, 2014). Great opportunities are important but not at the expense of your honesty and integrity. Organizations employ human resource professionals and tools to verify your information. Falsifying an application, cover letter, or résumé is grounds for termination. Make sure your résumé is repeatedly proof-read to eliminate spelling and grammar errors. It is common for interns to send out several résumés and cover letters. In doing so, be sure to tailor the documents accordingly, such as changing the name of the organization in the cover letter. Lack of attention to such detail will be apparent to the receiving organizations. Lastly, it is unlikely you will be asked to provide a curriculum vitae (CV) in place of a résumé, but here is some background just in case. A CV is an overview of your professional and academic history; it generally includes more detail than a résumé. As with résumés, you can use a basic template to help you get a CV started. The University of Pittsburgh Graduate School of Public Health provides guidance on the common sections of an effective CV: https://www.publichealth.pitt.edu/careers/job-search-tool-kit/resumes-and-curriculum-vitae/cv.

# Interviews

Interviews can be a worrisome experience for those who do not know what to expect. Luckily, much like résumé preparation, there are vast resources available to help students and job seekers with their preparation. If your academic institution does not offer access to Big Interview, you should check out the services on your own at biginterview.com. Big Interview offers video and interactive lessons on interview basics; mastering universal interview questions; behavioral interviewing; competency-based interviewing; common interview challenges, such as English as a second language; and more (Big Interview, 2020). You can also use the program to record your answers to common interview questions for later playback and critique. Professional organizations offer a variety of tools as well. ACHE offers a tool that allows subscribers to record their responses to expert-recommended questions. Recordings can later be shared with career coaches and mentors for feedback (ACHE, 2020b). This type of practice can help reduce anxiety associated with the uncertainties surrounding interviews.

Interview preparation is critical and personal. Even if you are comfortable answering typical questions about yourself and your unique qualifications, you must dedicate time to researching the organization with whom you are seeking an internship (or employment). You should understand the organization's mission, vision, and values. You should be able to describe how your work ethic aligns with these principles; therefore, having a copy of them with you at the interview is advised. Consider information shared on its website(s) to understand the organization's history and clients served. Organizations share information that is important to them on their websites, so be prepared to discuss this as well. You may even want to research articles or press releases written about the organization or speak to others employed by the organization to gain perspective (Makely, Austin, & Kester,

2017). Having trouble identifying internship opportunities? There are resources available to help you with this as well. Handshake is a platform that can connect students with employers seeking interns and new employees. Handshake can assist students with receiving personalized job recommendations related to their academic major and interests (Handshake, 2020).

When considering interview preparation, understand there are different types of interviews: employers may utilize telephone interviews, digital interviews using meeting technologies such as Skype or Zoom, face-to-face interviews, or a combination of interview modalities. Know you may be interviewed by a single person or a panel of people.

If your interviewers are going to see you, one of the first things you should consider is your appearance. Your first impression is critical; be sure to appear groomed and professional. While consensus on appropriate interview attire may not be unanimous, ample literature still supports a fairly traditional professional approach. This includes a suit and tie for men and a business suit or professional skirt and blouse for women (Makely, Austin, & Kester, 2017). As these suggestions may conflict with your personal style and comfort, be sure to find a balance that works for you. Remember, solid first impressions are vital. Have confidence and show enthusiasm!

What documents might you want to have on hand during an interview? Your interviewer or site coordinator may advise you about what to bring. If this is the case, make sure not to miss anything. If you aren't advised, be sure to have an up-to-date cover letter and résumé (tailored to respective internship experience). Kiser (2016) suggests printed versions be on high quality, neutral-colored paper. Other items to consider: immunization records; academic institution's internship manual, policies, and requirements; academic transcripts; your portfolio if you've prepared one; faculty contact information; and a list of questions you have about the organization and the internship experience (just in case you forget what you wanted to ask). Be sure to have a pen and paper with you to take notes.

You may also be asked to provide personal and/or professional references. Historically, reference checks were widely used in candidate selection processes, but their usefulness is becoming increasingly controversial (Fried & Fottler, 2018). Be aware that previous employers may be hesitant to provide information beyond job title and employment dates for liability reasons. Be sure your references have agreed to speak on your behalf in advance; they should not be surprised when the organization contacts them. Be sure to provide the organization with current, complete, and accurate information about your references.

As you meet your interviewers, remember to smile, be friendly, and be enthusiastic. Consider writing down the names of the people you are meeting with for later reference if you forget them. Eye contact with interviewers is important. During a panel interview, make eye contact with each member of the interview team. Look at each of them while you are speaking. If you are asked a question you don't fully understand, ask for clarification.

Utilizing interview prep tools such as those mentioned previously will help you prepare for common interview questions. To get you started, a few frequently asked questions are listed below (Makely, Austin, & Kester, 2017; McConnell, 2019; Malvey & Sapp, 2020). Note that we included some questions that pertain more to employment opportunities than to internships as you will eventually need to examine those as well. Remember, interviewers will be looking for general information about you as well as evaluating certain competencies (such as teamwork and decision making) and behaviors (such as how you've historically conducted yourself in specific situations that may be encountered during your internship). At times, job-knowledge questions may also be incorporated. For example, an operating room nurse intern or job applicant may be asked to recite appropriate things to ask a patient prior to surgery (Fried & Fottler, 2018) while laboratory students and professionals may be asked about their phlebotomy skills. Be sure to answer all questions honestly, thoughtfully, concisely, and enthusiastically. If you need clarification about a certain question (or statement), be sure to ask.

- Why are you interested in this internship/job? *Remember to demonstrate your research of the job and organization.*

- What do you know about this organization? *Again, remember to demonstrate your research of the organization; know their mission, vision, and values.*

- Articulate your professional strengths and weaknesses. *A word of caution about addressing your weakness(es): Don't be afraid to share your weaknesses; most will consider this an indication of self-awareness. That said, after you briefly describe your weakness, try to follow up with a narrative of how you are consciously working to improve upon what you have identified.*

- What do you think it would take to be successful in this internship/job? *Has the organization defined a particular need in the job description? Do you have the ability to uniquely fulfill the need?*

- Describe your career goals, both short and long term. *Organizations spend time and resources training interns. They may not be interested in pursuing candidates who are pursuing short-term opportunities.*

- Why should we select you over other applicants? *Use this as your opportunity to highlight your unique qualities. Again, remember your research. If possible, relate your distinctiveness to the internship/ job description and the organization.*

- Tell us about a time when you came up with a creative or innovative solution to a problem. *Try to provide an example of your problem-solving skills. Make your example as relevant to the internship/job description as possible.*

- Tell us about a time you led a team or worked as part of a team. *Provide examples and highlight skills you developed.*

- Describe a time when you had a conflict with a classmate/ professor/coworker. How did you handle the situation? If you could go back, would you do anything differently? *A word of advice about answering this one: be hesitant about criticizing previous colleagues (or employers); you do not want your character or disposition to be improperly judged.*

- How do you measure your professional success? *Of course, the answer to this question (and all questions) will be personal but here are a few avenues to consider: setting and achieving goals, helping others, fulfilling your professional mission, job satisfaction, motivation, and passion.*

- Why did you leave your last job? *Honesty is a good idea here. If you had a bad job experience or were let go from your previous position, accentuate what you learned and describe how the occurrence contributed to your growth. If you are seeking new opportunities, you may highlight what specifically about the organization attracts you.*

- Where do you see yourself in five years? *This may be another way to inquire about your future goals. Additionally, employers may be seeking individuals who are looking to make a sustaining commitment to an organization. Indicating you are seeking an opportunity with an organization that can facilitate your learning and growth is a good way to portray that you might be such an individual. If you are uncertain of your goals, at least be able to demonstrate that you have devoted a certain amount of time to considering the topic as opposed to simply stating that you are unsure.*

■ What questions do you have for us? *Surely you will have some related to the specific internship/job experience. You can also ask interviewers generic questions such as, "What do you enjoy most about working here?" to gain perspective about culture.*

■ If you were a fruit, which would you be and why? *Yes, you read that correctly. The University of Pittsburgh's Graduate School of Public Health's interview toolkit reminds students that employers may, on occasion, ask unusual questions to gauge applicant confidence and creativity (University of Pittsburgh, 2020).*

Respond to questions in a thorough, yet concise manner. Avoid nodding or shaking your head or use of slang (*yeah* and *nope*) in place of proper yes or no responses. If you catch yourself rambling (it can happen when you are nervous), make your point and finish your response. Avoid interrupting the interviewer(s). Need more practice? Big Interview provides expert interview question advice here: https://biginterview.com/job-interview-questions/.

Most interviewers in healthcare should be cognizant of appropriate interview behavior. Just in case, however, be sure to understand there are questions that should be avoided in the interview setting to reduce potential conscious and unconscious bias. Interviewers put themselves at potential legal risk if they inquire about candidates' age, date of birth, race, religion, national origin, disability status, marital status, or union membership as these items should not influence general hiring decisions (U.S. EEOC, 2020; McConnell, 2019). If you are asked questions probing for the information above, feel free to politely divert the conversation back to your ability to perform the essential functions of the internship/job. Keep in mind that inquiries could be inadvertent as conversations tend to get more casual, such as in settings where you are invited to lunch with your interview panel.

In the virtual interview setting, be sure to select a quiet location. Malvey and Sapp (2020) offer the following additional tips for successful digital interviews:

- Choose a location that has good lighting.

- Be intentional about what your interviewers can view behind you. Avoid excessive clutter and other distracting items.

- Consider headphones to reduce background noise.

- If using your smartphone: consider stabilizing it in a holder, ensure adequate charge, and disable alarms that could cause unnecessary distraction when they go off.

Here are some final thoughts about the interview process. If you are traveling for a face-to-face encounter, be sure to arrive to your interview on time. Lateness does not make the greatest first impression and it can cause you to be anxious. Parking at some healthcare organizations can be tricky; be sure to leave a few extra minutes for this or ask about parking in advance. Try not to be nervous; be yourself; take a few deep breaths if you need to. Remember to introduce yourself and motion for a handshake. Be sure to smile! An interview is a two-way street. While you are trying to sell yourself as the best candidate, you are also there to get your questions answered. Be sure to do so as this will help you decide if the opportunity will be a good fit for you. Recall that your résumé and interview answers must be honest depictions of you as an individual. That said, keep in mind some of the common attributes employers seek. These include professionalism, good communication skills, ability to work in teams, adaptability, integrity, reliability, creativity, compassion, humility, resiliency, critical thinking skills, time-management skills, ethical practice, vision, motivation, sincerity, enthusiasm, emotional intelligence, self-awareness and self-confidence, and potential for growth and learning agility (NCHL, 2021; LinkedIn, 2020; McConnell, 2019; Kaissi, 2018; Tipton, 2017; Makely, Badasch, & Chesebro, 2014).

Job interviewees are typically advised against being the first to bring up compensation packages (Malvey & Sapp, 2020). Although important, you do not want to portray this as your top interest. When the topic does arise, be sure you have done a little research to educate yourself about salaries for positions comparable to the ones you are applying for. Websites such as Payscale.com and Glassdoor.com can help you with this. An experienced interviewer will likely conclude the interview with a reasonable timeline of next steps, for example, when you will be contacted about a decision and by whom. If this information is not disclosed, feel free to inquire about next steps. As the interview concludes, if you have decided you want the position and believe you would be a good fit, be sure to make that clear.

After your interview, it is customary and good practice to send thank-you notes to your interviewers. Reaffirm your interest in the position. Lastly, remember to use resources available to you to help you prepare for the interview experience. Practice is essential but make sure you sound authentic and not rehearsed during actual exchanges.

# Job Applications

While this handbook is primarily about the internship process, the authors would be remiss if we did not touch on job applications. Completing a job application is an essential step in securing employment. Please remember that job applications are legal documents. Interns are advised to ensure their job application content aligns with their résumé and cover letter content. Double check places and dates of employment and contact information. If you have recently graduated, be sure your application indicates graduation date.

As with interns, criminal background checks may be completed on all potential employees. If you have been convicted of a crime, you are advised to disclose it. The employment application may have instructions on how to report such items. If so, read thoroughly and respond accordingly. Employers may be inclined to extend you an opportunity to explain your circumstances. Organizations such as SHRM have developed programs that inform and encourage second chances to people with criminal backgrounds (Gurchiek, 2019).

## RÉSUMÉ, COVER LETTER, AND INTERVIEW REMINDERS

- Be diligent and thorough in preparing your résumé for internship opportunities. You want to make a solid *and honest* first impression.

- Create résumés and cover letters that are tailored to individual organizations.

- Before your interview, be sure to practice. Be prepared, but make sure you won't sound rehearsed.

- Have you committed to an internship schedule that you can adhere to? Being on time and maintaining good attendance is critical to establishing a solid work ethic.

- Be self-aware and mindful of the resources available to you! Excelling personally and professionally takes practice and dedication!

---

### EXERCISE/JOURNAL PROMPT: RÉSUMÉ AND COVER LETTER

Your classmate Jane Doe has prepared a chronological résumé and cover letter for her internship preparation course and she has asked you to review it for her. See Appendix A. What feedback will you provide Jane, specifically?

Organize your thoughts on the Chapter 3 Journal Page provided or discuss in small groups (or both). Try to write at least 100 words.

---

### EXERCISE/JOURNAL PROMPT: GPA ON RÉSUMÉ

Maurer (2020) suggests that organizations may inadvertently create bias against students who are more likely to come from low-income households by setting minimum GPA hiring criteria for early careerists. What do you think about this?

Organize your thoughts on the Chapter 3 Journal Page provided or discuss in small groups (or both). Try to write at least 50 words.

# Chapter 3 Journal Page

# References

American College of Healthcare Executives (ACHE). (2020a). *Resume review service.* https://www.ache.org/career-resource-center/products-and-services/resume-review-critique-service

American College of Healthcare Executives (ACHE). (2020b). *ACHE's interview prep tool.* https://www.ache.org/career-resource-center/build-your-personal-brand/interview-prep-tool

American Health Information Management Association (AHIMA). (2019). http://www.ahima.org/searchresults?q=resume

Big Interview. (2020). *All the help you need to land the job.* https://biginterview.com/pricing/

CareerBuilder (2019). https://www.careerbuilder.com/

Enelow, W. (2018). *Resume-writing essentials: Five most powerful career summaries."* Society for Human Resource Management (SHRM). https://www.shrm.org/resourcesandtools/hr-topics/organizational-and-employee-development/pages/resume-writing-essentials-five-most-powerful-career-summaries.aspx

Enelow, W. (2020). *Leveraging keywords to advance your career.* Society for Human Resource Management. https://www.shrm.org/resourcesandtools/hr-topics/organizational-and-employee-development/pages/leveraging-keywords-to-advance-your-career.aspx

Enelow, W., & Kursmark, L. (2020). *How to write powerful and memorable HR resumes.* Society for Human Resource Management (SHRM). https://www.shrm.org/resourcesandtools/hr-topics/organizational-and-employee-development/pages/how-to-create-an-hr-resume.aspx

Fried, B. J., & Fottler, M. D. (2018). *Fundamentals of human resources in healthcare.* Chicago, IL: Health Administration Press.

Gurchiek, K. (2019). *Formerly incarcerated are an overlooked source of talent.* Society for Human Resource Management. https://www.shrm.org/resourcesandtools/hr-topics/behavioral-competencies/global-and-cultural-effectiveness/pages/formerly-incarcerated-are-an-overlooked-source-of-talent-.aspx

Handshake. (2020). *Overview.* https://www.joinhandshake.com/

Kaissi, A. (2018). *Intangibles: The unexpected traits of high-performing healthcare leaders.* Chicago, IL: Health Administration Press.

Kiser, P. M. (2016). *The Human services internship: Getting the most from your experience* (4th ed.). Boston, MA: Cengage Learning.

LinkedIn. (2020). *30 behavioral interview questions to identify high-potential candidates.* https://business.linkedin.com/content/dam/me/business/en-us/talent-solutions/resources/pdfs/linkedin-30-questions-to-identify-high-potential-candidates-ebook-8-7-17-uk-en.pdf

Lyden, M. (2009). *College students: Do this! Get hired!* Charleston, SC: www.DoThisGetHired.com.

Makely, S., Austin, V. J., & Kester, Q. (2017). *Professionalism in health care: A primer for career success* (5th ed.). Boston, MA: Pearson Education.

Makely, S., Badasch, S. A., & Chesebro, D. S. (2014). *Becoming a health care professional.* Upper Saddle River, NJ: Pearson Education.

Malvey, D., & Sapp, J. (2020). *Your healthcare job hunt: How your digital presence can make or break your career.* Chicago, IL: Health Administration Press.

Maurer, R. (2020). *8 diversity recruiting mistakes and how to avoid them.* Society for Human Resource Management. https://www.shrm.org/resourcesandtools/hr-topics/talent-acquisition/pages/8-diversity-recruiting-mistakes-how-to-avoid-them.aspx?utm_source=all&utm_medium=social&utm_campaign=communications~together_forward~8diversityrecruitingmistakes

McConnell, C. R. (2019). *The effective healthcare supervisor.* Burlington, MA: Jones and Bartlett Learning.

National Association of Colleges and Employers (NACE). (2020). *Career readiness resources: Sample materials.* https://www.naceweb.org/career-readiness/competencies/sample-materials/

National Center for Healthcare Leadership (NCHL). (2021). *NCHL Health Leadership Competency Model 3.0.* https://www.nchl.org/research/#NCHL_Health_Leadership_Competency_Model_30

Rosser, L. (2017). *A veteran's guide to developing a resume.* National Association of Colleges and Employers (NACE). https://www.naceweb.org/career-readiness/best-practices/the-veterans-guide-to-developing-a-resume/

Smith, A., & Berg, M. (2020). Business professionals' rankings of applicants' resumes: Updated considerations for resume instruction. *Journal of Business Strategies, 37*(1), 55–80.

Tipton, D. (2017). *Personal and professional growth for health care professionals.* Burlington, MA: Jones and Bartlett Learning.

University of Pittsburgh Graduate School of Public Health. (2020). *Preparing for your interview.* https://www.publichealth.pitt.edu/careers/job-search-tool-kit/preparing-for-your-interview

U.S. Equal Employment Opportunity Commission (EEOC). (2020). *Employees & job applicants.* https://www.eeoc.gov/employees-job-applicants

Yate, M. Do the standard rules of resume writing still apply? (2020). *HRNews.* https://www.shrm.org/resourcesandtools/hr-topics/organizational-and-employee-development/career-advice/pages/do-the-standard-rules-of-resume-writing-still-apply.aspx

# 4

# PROFESSIONAL COMMUNICATION

## Overview

Chapter 4 is an important chapter about professional communication. It covers social media, portfolios, writing and speaking skills, soft skills, and bedside manner. Proper, professional, and respectful communication is essential in the healthcare workplace. Individuals who strive to understand, practice, and master these dynamics can realize resounding benefits, both personally and professionally.

## Social Media

Potential employers may seek to find information about internship/job candidates online. A 2016 CareerBuilder survey of 2,186 hiring managers revealed that 60% of employers reported researching job candidates on social media (Fried & Fottler, 2018). Malvey and Sapp (2020) contend that more than half of employers will not hire a candidate who does not have an online presence. Literature suggests some healthcare employers ask applicants to log into their social media accounts to display content to interviewers (Makely, Austin, & Kester, 2017). While this interviewing tactic may be debatable, awareness is key. You should consider using your social media accounts, such as LinkedIn, to your advantage. Keep your profiles professional, accurate, updated, and consistent with the information shared on your résumé and cover letter. Further, you may want to avoid posting negative comments about topics such as healthcare, healthcare organizations, previous employers, coworkers, and clients. You may also want to consider whether items you post could be viewed as discriminatory (Fried & Fottler, 2018). Malvey and Sapp (2020) suggest keeping business and personal accounts for platforms such as Facebook separate. Consider deleting past pictures or posts you would deem inappropriate for a potential employer to view.

# Portfolios

Portfolios are a collection of materials that represent one's knowledge, skills, accomplishments, and distinguishedness. Portfolios are not routinely required in interviews but having one may set you apart from other candidates. Employers may be impressed by students who dedicate the time to preparing samples of their work. Portfolio creation can also be a great exercise in reflection for the creator. If you choose to compile a portfolio (or if it was a component of your coursework), common items include samples of coursework, awards, performance evaluations, volunteer commitments, and final projects/practicums/thesis papers.

Although there are many types of portfolios, some literature suggests the use of electronic portfolios (ePortfolios) (Sweitzer & King, 2019; Kiser, 2016). An example of ePortfolio software available at no cost to students is Mahara, which can be accessed at https://mahara.org. Another useful online resource is eportfolios.org (Kiser, 2016).

# Writing and Speaking Skills

Hopefully, after reading about résumés, cover letters, and interviews, you are already convinced that writing and speaking are important. Healthcare interns and professionals are often called upon to write various professional pieces. These include, but are not limited to, job descriptions, policies, performance reviews, interview questions, letters of appointment or rejection, media releases, electronic health record entries, and journal articles. Effective writing, like most skills, requires practice, diligence, and patience. According to a 2018 NACE student survey, three-fourths of students reported that their internship experience positively impacted their oral and written communication skills (NACE, 2018). As with résumé writing and interviewing, know there are multiple resources available to help writers become more effective. Here are some basic tips to consider (Baird, 2008; Faigley, 2016):

- Recognize that reading facilitates writing. For example, if you are trying to write a great résumé, you may want to begin by reading several sample résumés.

- Seek feedback. Invite others to read your work and welcome suggestions. You might be pleasantly surprised how multiple perspectives can strengthen a written piece. Proofreading is always encouraged.

- Choose words deliberately and strive for clarity and conciseness.

- Understand your audience. Healthcare is a diverse industry of clinical and nonclinical and technical and nontechnical professionals. If addressing multiple groups simultaneously, for example in a company-wide memo, you must use language that can be understood by all.

- Be cognizant of and sensitive to stereotypes and biases. This topic will be discussed again in chapter 6. Reflecting on audience should help with this.

- Ensure your electronic communications are coming from a professional address.

Remember the importance of citation and formatting styles when writing. The Purdue University Online Writing Lab (OWL) is a great resource to consult for this: https://owl.purdue.edu/owl/purdue_owl.html.

Many of the tips that apply to writing, such as audience, biases, and clarity, also apply to speaking. Aside from interview etiquette and daily face-to-face and telephone encounters with colleagues and clients, interns should evaluate their ability to speak in front of groups. You may be afforded the opportunity to present a project, paper, or piece of research you worked on as part of your experiential learning. This is a great time to shine! The following speaking recommendations were derived from the work of professional speaker Laura Stack (2013):

- Consider how you will capture and retain your audience's attention.

- Be conscious of your body language and voice. For example, your tone and the rapidness with which you speak can impression your listeners.

- Try to minimize filler words such as *um*.

- Be cognizant of start, break, and stop times. These items may be designated by an agenda.

- Although you do not want your presentation to sound rehearsed, a respectable level of rehearsal and preparation is advised.

# Soft Skills and Bedside Manner

Hopefully, you learned a little about soft skills in the classroom setting; these attributes are extremely important in a service industry workplace such as healthcare. Soft skills are the characteristics that shape your interactions with others; examples include collaboration, communication, confidence, honesty, listening, resilience, critical thinking, problem solving, prioritization, creativity, adaptability, leadership, and potential for growth (Tulgan, 2015; Weiss, 2019; LinkedIn, 2020). As an individual and a professional, it is important to reflect on these attributes and understand there are resources available to help you develop these skills. Deliberate efforts to do so will likely have a direct positive impact on your personal and professional relationships, including relationships with patients (if you work in patient contact areas). If you think you are particularly strong in any of these areas, remember to say so in your résumé or cover letter. While entire books are written on soft skills, here are a few tips to consider (Kamin, 2013; Makely, Austin, & Kester, 2017):

- Verify that others have received your message when you communicate. For example, if you were giving directions to a patient, you could ask them to repeat or confirm your message in their own words. This is sometimes referred to as two-way communication.

- Literature suggests that up to 90% of communication is nonverbal. Be conscious of your nonverbal cues, such as body language and facial expressions.

- Think before you speak. Don't say something out of anger that you'll later regret.

- Respond to colleagues respectfully.

- Remember to say "please" and "thank you" regularly.

- Give credit where credit is due.

- Listen actively and intently. Try not to interrupt others as they are speaking.

- Respect others' views.

- Be cautious of terms of endearment such as honey or sweetie, as some may find them offensive.

If your internship experience includes contact with patients, you will be expected to integrate various concepts discussed in this handbook into your interactions with them. Examples discussed thus far include adherence to confidentiality and exemplification of appropriate soft skills. If patient encounters make you anxious, no worries. Like most skills, patient interactions can be practiced. Visualize scenarios in your mind if that helps. People generally desire to be treated as individuals, and individuals have personal needs and generally value respect, dignity, and compassion (Roberts, 2015). Remembering these basic values can help you immensely. Mindfulness of the platinum rule is advised as well: "Treat others the way they want to be treated" (Ellenbogen, Connolly, & Meyer, 2020).

## PROFESSIONAL COMMUNICATION REMINDERS

- Consider your social media presence. Is it appropriate for a potential employer to view?

- Seeking feedback is always wise as meaningful suggestions can be critical to your personal and professional growth. Feedback on your writing is no different.

- Practice your soft skills, such as active listening, often!

## EXERCISE/JOURNAL PROMPT: TWO-WAY COMMUNICATION

You are interning with the director of the sonography department in a large, multihospital healthcare system. You planned to work on a customer satisfaction report this week but got called to assist with the Joint Commission inspection process with your preceptor at another hospital. The customer service report needs to be completed by 5 p.m. on Friday of the current week, so your preceptor has asked you to hand the project off to your fellow intern, Jane. From a single, casual conversation, you know Jane is older than you and has more health-care experience. Other than that, you two really have not interacted. Describe, in depth, your communication process to Jane.

Organize your thoughts on the Chapter 4 Journal Page provided or discuss in small groups (or both). Try to write at least 100 words.

# Chapter 4 Journal Page

# References

Baird, B. N. (2008). *The internship, practicum, and field placement handbook: A guide for the helping professions* (5th ed.). Upper Saddle River, NJ: Pearson/Prentice Hall.

Ellenbogen, R., Connolly, E., & Meyer, F. (2020). Maintenance of certification and the platinum rule. *Mayo Clinic Proceedings*, *95*(2), 228–230.

Faigley, L. (2016). *Writing: A guide for college and beyond*. Boston, MA: Pearson Education.

Fried, B. J., & Fottler, M. D. (2018). *Fundamentals of human resources in healthcare*. Chicago, IL: Health Administration Press.

Kamin, M. (2013). *Soft skills revolution: A guide for connecting with compassion for trainers, teams, and leaders*. San Francisco, CA: John Wiley & Sons.

Kiser, P.M. (2016). *The human services internship: Getting the most from your experience* (4th ed.). Boston, MA: Cengage Learning.

Ledlow, G. R., & Stephens, J. H. (2018). *Leadership for health professionals: Theory, skills, and applications*. Burlington, MA: Jones and Bartlett Learning.

LinkedIn. (2020). *30 behavioral interview questions to identify high-potential candidates*. https://business.linkedin.com/content/dam/me/business/en-us/talent-solutions/resources/pdfs/linkedin-30-questions-to-identify-high-potential-candidates-ebook-8-7-17-uk-en.pdf

Makely, S., Austin, V. J., & Kester, Q. (2017). *Professionalism in health care: A primer for career success* (5th ed.). Boston, MA: Pearson Education.

Malvey, D., & Sapp, J. (2020). *Your healthcare job hunt: How your digital presence can make or break your career*. Chicago, IL: Health Administration Press.

National Association of Colleges and Employers (NACE). (2018). *Students: Internships positively impact competencies*. https://www.naceweb.org/career-readiness/internships/students-internships-positively-impact-competencies/

Roberts, G. W. (2015). *Appreciative healthcare practice: A guide to compassionate, person-centreed care*. London: M&K Update Ltd.

Stack, L. (2013). *Supercompetent speaking: Lessons learned after 20 years as a professional speaker on creating killer presentations*. Highlands Ranch, CO: Productivity Pro.

Sweitzer, H. F., & King, M. A. (2019). *The successful internship: Personal, professional, and civic development in experiential learning.* Boston, MA: Cengage Learning.

Tulgan, B. (2015). *Bridging the soft skills gap: How to teach the missing basics to today's young talent.* Hoboken, NJ: John Wiley & Sons.

Weiss, L. (2019). *Viewpoint: The case for soft skills."* Society for Human Resource Management. https://www.shrm.org/resourcesandtools/hr-topics/organizational-and-employee-development/pages/viewpoint-the-case-for-soft-skills-.aspx

# 5

# PROFESSIONAL BEHAVIOR

## Overview

Professionalism is expected at all times during your internship. You are representing your academic institution and the organization where you are an intern. Chapter 5 delineates the expectations of acceptable behavior for interns. Specific attributes addressed include attendance and punctuality, time management, attire, etiquette, and conflict resolution. Remember, as an intern, you are a guest at your clinical site, and you should strive to make an impactful impression. Developing good habits during your internship will serve you well as you begin your professional career in healthcare.

## Attendance and Punctuality

Just as it was in school, during the interview process, and will be when you begin your career, attendance and punctuality are vital during your internship experience. Punctuality and good attendance will help ensure that you not only make a good impression of yourself but will also contribute to maximization of the time you get to spend with people who have dedicated themselves to teaching you. Literature cites poor attendance as a common reason for employee termination; therefore, it is never too early to develop good habits and exhibit a solid work ethic (Makely, Austin, & Kester, 2017).

# Time Management

Literature suggests effective time management skills can enhance your job satisfaction, productivity, and interpersonal relations (McConnell, 2019). As such, be conscious about planning; prioritizing; establishing goals, objectives, and deadlines; and reducing procrastination. These skills may not come naturally and will, therefore, need to be practiced! Weeks and Chan (2004) offer the following suggestions for optimizing personal time management:

- Try to identify your strengths and weaknesses related to time management. For instance, are you good at establishing deadlines or is this an area for improvement?

- Identify your personal time wasters such as unnecessary socializing, poor organization, and procrastination.

- Create a realistic time management action plan to facilitate positive change.

# Attire

Attire during your internship will most likely be directed by organizational dress code policy. Be sure to understand and adhere to the policies likely communicated with you before or during orientation. If you have questions, be sure to ask. Remember, you may seek employment at your internship site in the future, so you want to maintain a positive, professional impression. You should not have to spend a lot of money on a new wardrobe; second-hand stores are often a budget-conscious option. Make sure your appearance is clean and relatively wrinkle free. Be advised that some health care organizations do not allow open-toed shoes or strong fragrances to be worn.

# Etiquette

Remember to demonstrate good manners during your internship. Say "please," "thank you," and "excuse me" when appropriate. Remember to smile. Address people according to title, for example, Dr. Smith. Greet people in the hallways. If someone looks lost, offer to help them locate their desired destination. Chewing gum and using personal cell phones may violate organizational policy.

Some interns are fortunate enough to be invited to attend formal events such as business dinners or dinner meetings. These settings can be slightly uncomfortable if you have not encountered them before. Below are some etiquette tips:

- Determine if seats are assigned or if you are free to sit anywhere.

- Be prepared to mingle.

- Once seated, introduce yourself to (at least) the people on either side of you. Tell them you are an intern and are excited to be attending the event. Having a short elevator pitch about yourself in mind is a good idea.

- Place the (likely) linen napkin in your lap.

- If the meal is plated (as opposed to a buffet), the server will bring your food to the table, usually beginning with soup or salad. Consider waiting to eat until everyone at your table has received that specific course.

- You may have several forks and spoons, a different one for each course of the meal. Begin by using the outermost utensil first (Thomas, 2017).

- When you are finished with a course, leave the utensil on the plate and your server will pick it up. You may be asked if you wish to keep your knife. If so, you may place it back on the table for future use. Continue to use the outermost utensil until all courses have been served.

- If there is something on the table you would like to use, such as salad dressing, ask someone to pass it to you. Do not reach over people. The passing may happen naturally, usually to the right.

- There may be community butter on the table. At the head of your place setting, there may be a small butter knife. Use that to place some butter on your bread plate. Do not put your fork or dirty knife into the butter dish.

- At the top of your place setting, there may be another small fork or spoon; that is for dessert.

- Remember to chew with your mouth closed and do not talk with food in your mouth.

- Alcohol may be served at these events, sometimes for an additional cost. If you are of legal drinking age and wish to responsibly have a drink, be prepared to pay for it. Be cautious about such decisions: consider how you will be getting home and be sure to maintain your professionalism.

- Remember to observe, learn, network, and enjoy yourself!

## Conflict Resolution

While most experiential learning opportunities are positive and relatively free of major conflict, occasionally incidents happen (as listed in Chapter 2). It is important to understand both your university's and healthcare organization's conflict resolution policies. These policies will likely dictate that you communicate issues with your site and/or faculty coordinator initially, but you should also have a general sense of the hierarchy of people available to help you when these individuals cannot meet or have not met your needs. In addition to adhering to such policies and understanding that different styles of conflict resolution exist (Turnbull, 2016), Baird and Mollen (2019) offer the following helpful tips:

- Understand that occasional conflict is inevitable.

- Conflict can be a learning experience. If you reflect on such matters, you can begin to understand how you react to conflict and resolve to be a better participant in effective conflict resolution moving forward.

- Be sure to try to examine your role in conflict. For example, do you have trouble accepting constructive criticism from or acknowledging valid points made by others?

- Be sure to communicate your concerns and opinions and be receptive to actively listening to the concerns and opinions of others. Build on each other's ideas!

- Seeking the opinion of an impartial party about a conflict may be a valuable option for gaining perspective.

Should conflict arise during your internship, be sure to notify both your site and faculty coordinators. Avoid conflict in front of patients. In contentious situations, remain calm, professional, and respectful. Conflict with your site coordinator should be reported to your faculty coordinator as soon as possible. In their book *Crucial Conversations: Tools for Talking when Stakes are High*, Patterson, Grenny, McMillan, and Switzler (2012) offer dialogue advice related to such difficult topics as sexual harassment, authority issues, trust issues, and insubordination.

## PROFESSIONAL BEHAVIOR REMINDERS

- Be on time!

- Practice using your time effectively.

- Conflict can arise in the workplace. Be accountable for your part in conflict and know who to consult for advice and assistance in conflict resolution.

## EXERCISE/JOURNAL PROMPT: CONFLICT RESOLUTION

Multiple conflict style models exist. Models by Ledlow and Stephens (2018) and Sweitzer and King (2019) have three styles in common: accommodating, collaborating, and compromising. As the name implies, the accommodating individual may forgo his or her goals in favor of preserving relationships or harmony. Collaborating individuals tend to seek integrative solutions that satisfy the needs of both (or all) conflicting parties (Ledlow & Stephens, 2018; Sweitzer & King, 2019). Lastly, the compromising conflict style, again as the name implies, often results in each party getting some of their goals satisfied (or getting some of the things they wanted, usually at the expense of also giving something up).

Reflect not only on which of the three styles described here you believe you exhibit most commonly but also on the circumstances under which each style may be most appropriate and effective.

Organize your thoughts on the Chapter 5 Journal Page provided or discuss in small groups (or both). Try to write at least 100 words.

# Chapter 5 Journal Page

# References

Baird, B. N., & Mollen, Debra. (2019). *The internship, practicum, and field placement handbook: A guide for the helping professions* (8th ed.). New York, NY: Taylor & Francis.

Ledlow, G. R., & Stephens, J. H. (2018). *Leadership for health professionals: Theory, skills, and applications.* Burlington, MA: Jones and Bartlett Learning.

Makely, S., Austin, V. J., & Kester, Q. (2017). *Professionalism in health care: A primer for career success* (5th ed.). Boston, MA: Pearson Education.

McConnell, C. R. (2019). *The effective healthcare supervisor.* Burlington, MA: Jones and Bartlett Learning.

Patterson, K., Grenny, J., McMillan, R., & Switzler, A. (2012). *Crucial conversations: Tools for talking when stakes are high.* New York, NY: McGraw Hill.

Sweitzer, H. F., & King, M. A. (2019). *The successful internship: Personal, professional, and civic development in experiential learning.* Boston, MA: Cengage Learning.

Thomas, R. J. (2017). *Excuse me: The survival guide to modern business etiquette.* New York, NY: AMACOM.

Turnbull, H. (2016). *The illusion of inclusion: Global inclusion, unconscious bias, and the bottom line.* New York, NY: Business Expert Press.

Weeks, M., & Chan, J. (2004). *Taking control with time management: EBook edition* (5th ed.). New York, NY: AMACOM.

# 6

# DIVERSITY, INCLUSION, AND EQUITY IN THE WORKPLACE

## Overview

Chapter 6 covers the ever-important topics of diversity, inclusion, and equity in the workplace. Interns are advised to seek self-awareness concerning these topics and are expected to treat all people with respect and dignity. Knowledge of these essential topics can profoundly impact an individual's perception of self and others, thus influencing workplace dynamics and relationships.

## Workplace Diversity and Self-Awareness

Diversity in the workplace is also a topic you likely encountered in your coursework. As a healthcare professional, you must be prepared to work with diverse groups of employees and patients. Healthcare organizations serve clients from varying ethnic, age, and other groups daily and therefore require corresponding client-centered services to accommodate diverging needs. U.S. Census Bureau data project more than half of the U.S. population will belong to a minority group by 2044 (Colby & Ortman, 2015).

Diversity is a broad term that can refer to differences in race, ethnicity, age, socioeconomic status, political perspectives, geographic location, sexual preference, and more (Fried & Fottler, 2018). In addition to these attributes, there are varying personality types to consider. The literature surrounding these topics is vast, but the key concept for interns and new workforce entrants to remember is that differences exist. You will inevitably be called upon to work with individuals who differ from you in various ways. Be sure to maintain an open mind and treat these experiences as learning opportunities. *New York Times* best-selling author Kai-Fu Lee says, "The beauty of human beings lies in our diversity" (2018, p. 222). Author Geraldine Hynes contends, "Diversity in the workplace is a competitive advantage" (2015, p. xii).

Literature suggests that a keen sense of self-awareness can lead to a greater appreciation of diversity (Baird, 2008) on a personal level. Like other subjects discussed in this handbook, you are advised to understand your strengths and weaknesses related to the topic and the relevant resources available to you. Many professional organizations offer best practices, toolkits, and other resources related to diversity and cultural competence in the workplace. Sweitzer and King (2019) describe culture as a collection of beliefs and behaviors held by a group. The Institute for Diversity and Health Equity is one example. This organization offers web resources such as podcasts, blogs, videos, and webinars on topics such as diversity and inclusion and health equity and value (IDHE, 2020). Consider these key strategies for successful navigation of workplace diversity and increased cultural competence (Fried & Fottler, 2018; Sweitzer & King, 2019):

- Be aware of your own culture and cultural norms. Consideration of the cultural subgroups you belong to can be helpful here. Examples include race, ethnicity, age (generation), social class, and even your status as a college student. Cultural variables that may be evident in the workplace may include attitudes related to work, perception of time, definitions of success, and response to authority (Kiser, 2016).

- Acknowledge that prejudices and stereotypes exist and can be managed with practice.

- Appreciate exposure to and enrichment by cultures that differ from yours.

- Expect initial discomfort when dealing with people who are different from you.

Turnbull (2016) synergizes on the above with these additional suggestions:

- Actively listen for diverging frames of reference with an open mind. Active listening involves mindfully trying to receive the complete message being communicated.

- Demonstrate willingness to experiment with change to meet the needs of a diverse group. As a first step, consider joining a group that stretches your comfort zone, one that you may not have envisioned yourself joining in the past.

- Value diversity as an asset.

- Embrace and leverage innovation and creativity.

- Be intentional about using the individual strengths of team members synergistically.

# Equity

Arespacochaga and Robinson (2020, p. 1) assert health equity "is about creating a system where all individuals have equitable access to quality health outcomes" and reinforce consideration of structural barriers and limitations on health, including access to nutritious food, environmental quality, and viable housing, transportation, education, and employment. Barriers that prevent individuals from being able to access healthcare have been referred to as social determinants of health. The World Health Organization (WHO, 2020) defines social determinants as conditions in which people are born, grow, work, live and age, and the broader set of influences that shape lifestyles. Individuals and organizations can enhance their understanding of social determinants and equip themselves with knowledge to overcome such obstacles by familiarizing themselves with tools provided by organizations such as the Centers for Medicare and Medicaid Services (CMS) and the American Hospital Association (AHA).

# Diversity, Inclusion, and Equity—Organizationally and Beyond

To maximize the benefits of organizational diversity, organizations must also prioritize inclusion. Taylor (2020, p. 2) asserts, "Diversity should never be the final goal." Instead, employers should strive for a culture that promotes inclusion of the diverse workforce in opportunities that advance the outcomes and success of the organization. The Mayo Clinic has been recognized repeatedly by DiversityInc as a top hospital and health system for its commitments to diversity and inclusion (Mayo Clinic, 2020). One of its initiatives has been to develop Mayo Employee Resource Groups (MERGs), designed to celebrate and support diverse employee groups. The Mayo Clinic provides financial and administrative assistance to support each group's activities and overall success. Examples of current MERGs include African Descendants (AD); Greater Leadership Opportunities for Women (GLOW); Lesbian, Gay, Bisexual, Transgender, Intersex (LGBTI); Multicultural Nurses; and Veterans (Mayo Clinic, 2020). If you intern or work at an organization that has cultivated similar offerings, be sure to capitalize on opportunities that resonate with you. Taylor (2020) offers ways organizations can demonstrate commitment to equity and inclusion:

- Incorporate diversity and inclusion into organizational core values and prioritize measurement of impact.

- Ensure that inclusive hiring and promoting are embraced at all levels organizationally, including governing boards and senior executives. Diverse talent acquisition teams and interview panels can be effective.

- Encourage open dialogue about sensitive topics such as racism.

Handtke, Schilgen, and Mösko (2019) urge professionals to also consider diversity in healthcare concurrently in the social, cultural, and political realms. They offer the following strategies for implementing and providing culturally competent care:

- Conducting needs assessments. These can be done at various levels, beginning locally. They are considered a best practice in the development of diversity training programs as they provide a foundation for identifying disparities and a baseline upon which trainings can be tailored (King, Gulick, & Avery, 2010).

- Offering cultural competence trainings

- Offering interpreter services. Language barriers have been linked to patients leaving the medical setting or not returning for follow-up services (Purnell, 2014).

- Enhancing the use of Telemedicine

- Developing culturally and linguistically diverse materials

- Fostering community health networks

## DIVERSITY, INCLUSION, AND EQUITY REMINDERS

- Expect to be challenged by new experiences and relationships with people (perhaps including patients) who differ from you. Embrace and learn from these opportunities!

- Be self-aware and mindful of the resources available to you! Excelling personally and professionally takes practice and dedication!

## EXERCISE/JOURNAL PROMPT: WORKPLACE INCLUSION

Rajesh (2018) contends employees should feel safe to express dissent in workplace settings. Describe a scenario where this may be applicable in healthcare.

Organize your thoughts on the Chapter 6 Journal Page provided or discuss in small groups (or both). Try to write at least 100 words.

## EXERCISE/JOURNAL PROMPT: DIVERSITY AND INCLUSION PERSONAL EXPERIENCE

Reflect on a diversity-related issue you have encountered or that you perceive as prominent around you. This can be in your hometown, your academic institution, your place of employment, or another area of importance to you.

Organize your thoughts on the Chapter 6 Journal Page provided or discuss in small groups (or both). Try to write at least 100 words.

## EXERCISE/JOURNAL PROMPT: DIVERSITY AND INCLUSION AND NETWORKING

In her book *Diversity on the Executive Path: Wisdom and Insights for Navigating to the Highest Levels of Healthcare Leadership,* Diane Dixon (2020) suggests that individuals should strive for a mix of same-race and cross-race networking relationships. She believes that same-race interactions facilitate psychological support and that support for managing racial barriers and cross-race interactions can add information that may not be available or conceptualized in same-race circles. Considering this information, imagine you are interning for the week with the chief diversity officer (CDO) in a large hospital that has recently acquired a small rural hospital. The CDO asks you to suggest specific training or other activities that may facilitate such networking opportunities for employees interested in strengthening their networks. What might you suggest?

Organize your thoughts on the Chapter 6 Journal Page provided or discuss in small groups (or both). Try to write at least 100 words.

## EXERCISE/JOURNAL PROMPT: PERSONALITY TYPES

Ledlow and Stephens (2018) describe type A individuals as competitive, inquisitive, and occasionally impatient. Conversely, type B individuals tend to be relaxed, easygoing, and more social. Which of these types do you identify more with? How do you think you will adjust to working with people who are the opposite personality type? Note: some individuals exhibit characteristics of both types.

Organize your thoughts on the Chapter 6 Journal Page provided or discuss in small groups (or both). Try to write at least 100 words.

# Chapter 6 Journal Page

# References

Arespacochaga, E., & Robinson, D. (2020). *Breaking down barriers to greater health equity.* American Hospital Association. https://www.aha.org/news/blog/2020-07-20-breaking-down-barriers-greater-health-equity

Baird, B. N. (2008). *The internship, practicum, and field placement handbook: A guide for the helping professions* (5th ed.). Upper Saddle River, NJ: Pearson/Prentice Hall.

Colby, S. L., & Ortman, J. M. (2015). Projections of the size and composition of the U.S. population: 2014 to 2060. U.S. Census Bureau. https://www.census.gov/content/dam/Census/library/publications/2015/demo/p25-1143.pdf

Dixon, D. (2020). *Diversity on the executive path: Wisdom and insights for navigating to the highest levels of healthcare leadership.* Chicago, IL: Health Administration Press.

Fried, B. J., & Fottler, M. D. (2018). *Fundamentals of human resources in healthcare.* Chicago, IL: Health Administration Press.

Handtke, O., Schilgen, B., & Mösko, M. (2019). Culturally competent healthcare: A scoping review of strategies implemented in healthcare organizations and a model of culturally competent healthcare provision. *PloS One, 14*(7), e0219971.

Hynes, G. (2015). *Get along, get it done, get ahead: Interpersonal communication in the diverse workplace.* 1st ed. New York, NY: Business Expert Press.

Institute for Diversity and Health Equity (IDHE). (2020). https://ifdhe.aha.org/

King, E., Gulick, L., & Avery, D. (2010). The divide between diversity training and diversity education: Integrating best practices. *Journal of Management Education, 34*(6), 891–906.

Kiser, P. M. (2016). *The human services internship: Getting the most from your experience* (4th ed.). Boston, MA: Cengage Learning.

Ledlow, G. R., & Stephens, J. H. (2018). *Leadership for health professionals: Theory, skills, and applications.* Burlington, MA: Jones and Bartlett Learning.

Lee, Kai-Fu. (2018). *AI superpowers: China, Silicon Valley, and the new world order.* Boston, MA: Houghton Mifflin Harcourt.

Mayo Clinic. (2020). *Mayo employee resource groups.* https://www.mayoclinic.org/about-mayo-clinic/office-diversity-inclusion/our-employees/mayo-employee-resource-groups-mergs

Purnell, L. D. (2014). *Guide to culturally competent health care* (3rd. ed.). Philadelphia, PA: F. A. Davis Company.

Rajesh, S. (2018). The 99 day diversity challenge: Creating an inclusive workplace. In *The 99 Day Diversity Challenge*. SAGE Publications.

Sweitzer, H. F., & King, M. A. (2019). *The successful internship: Personal, professional, and civic development in experiential learning.* Boston, MA: Cengage Learning.

Taylor, J. C. (2020). *Driving out bias should start in the C-Suite.* Society for Human Resource Management (SHRM). https://www.shrm.org/hr-today/news/hr-news/Pages/Driving-Out-Bias-Should-Start-in-the-C-Suite.aspx

Turnbull, H. (2016). *The illusion of inclusion: Global inclusion, unconscious bias, and the bottom line.* New York, NY: Business Expert Press.

World Health Organization. (2020). *Social determinants of health.* https://www.who.int/social_determinants/en/

# 7

# CONCLUDING THE INTERNSHIP

## Overview

Chapter 7 shares ideas about concluding the internship and making your last impression with your clinical site a positive one. This chapter examines evaluations, reflection, letters of thanks, networking, self-care, job-seeking, and personal mission, vision, and values. Congratulations!! You are at the end of your experiential learning journey; hopefully, you have gained invaluable insight into the world of healthcare. Be sure to finish strong, reflect, and be grateful for those who have invested their time, talent, and resources into mentoring you throughout your academic journey. The authors wish you a successful career in the industry they have great passion for! We challenge you to be empowered, embrace change, and give your best to the communities and patients you serve!

## Evaluations

At the conclusion of your internship and throughout, you were evaluated on your knowledge and performance. Hopefully, you found the feedback you received invaluable. Faculty and site coordinators can benefit from student evaluations as well. Take advantage of opportunities to evaluate your preceptors and their respective programs as your input can be utilized to strengthen experiences for future students. Literature suggests exit interviews are an internship best practice as they provide organizations with opportunities to solicit student feedback

(NACE, 2020). Take advantage of such opportunities if afforded to you; this will give you a chance to share your opinions about your experiences. If you are leaving your internship site for employment elsewhere, you are advised to exit on positive terms. Burnette and Evans (2020) write about controlling exit narratives and urge individuals to "leave them laughing and wanting you back" (p. 233).

Although site coordinators have the opportunity to evaluate intern performance, it is likely the faculty coordinator who determines the final internship grade. Inherently, site coordinator feedback will be incorporated into final grade determination. Interns are advised to accept feedback in a humble manner; avoid getting defensive. Constructive criticism is conveyed to help you.

# Reflection

Reflection is an excellent habit to develop as related to self-awareness. Your aspirations to learn and become your best self should be perpetual. Ghaye and Lillyman (2010) explain how reflection can be used to help individuals advance their thinking and practice by confronting personal and professional shortcomings. They assert, "Reflection is an integral part of experiential learning and the development of practical knowledge" (p. 60). Daniel Goleman (2005) links self-awareness, emotional intelligence, and empathy to enhanced work, relationships, and health. Self-awareness has also been acknowledged as a revered leadership quality (Frisina, 2014).

As you are nearing the end of your internship experience, reflection upon various constructs should be inherent. Reflect upon your overall experience, what you learned, what you would still like to learn, your decision making skills, and what your career aspirations are. In his book *Drive: The Surprising Truth About What Motivates Us*, Daniel Pink (2009) encourages individuals to reflect on their intrinsic motivators—the activities that bring an inherent sense of purpose and fulfillment. Harris (2016) links motivation to empowerment.

Reflection can be used on the job as well. For example, after implementation of a new process, procedure, or new piece of technology, it is common to reflect on a project so that future projects may run more effectively. Makely, Austin, and Kester (2017) offer journaling as an effective reflective method. If you prefer a structured reflection, Thistlethwait and McKimm (2016) suggest the following prompts:

- Describe what happened.

- Describe your thoughts and feelings as this can enhance self-awareness.

- Evaluate the event. Note what you perceived as good and bad.

- Formulate conclusions.

- Conceptualize an action plan that includes how you will proceed and what you might change or do differently in the future.

Attempt journal entries pertaining to the above criteria at least three times: early in your internship experience (first couple of weeks), midway through, and near the end of your journey. Burnett and Evans (2020) recommend daily journaling of simple items such as what you learned, what you initiated, and who you helped.

# Letters of Thanks

At the conclusion of your internship, you have hopefully interacted with multiple professionals at your academic institution and healthcare organization that deserve thanks. Be sure to thank them for their respective contributions to your personal and professional growth. This is a concept to keep with you throughout your career. Everyone appreciates a little thanks now and again; a little appreciation can go a long way. Maybe you will even inspire others to do the same.

# Networking

Networking can be fundamental to securing a job and advancing your career in healthcare. Be sure to interact with a variety of people in different settings to gain perspective and form relationships with people you can trust and who can strengthen your support system. Johns (2017) urges professionals to seek networks that include people with expertise, influence, the ability to challenge you, and the wherewithal to hold you accountable.

Establishing a sound online presence via professional social media accounts is one way to expand your network. Embracing formal or informal opportunities to work with and sustain relationships with mentors or executive coaches is highly recommended (Dixon, 2020).

Attending professional conferences and joining professional and/ or humanitarian organizations are also encouraged. Keep in touch with your classmates; they may communicate job opportunities in the future, provide references, or become colleagues. Don't forget alumni networks from your academic institution! Susan RoAne (2016) offers these tips for face-to-face networking and reminds readers that, like most skills, networking takes practice:

- Plan ahead. You may want to preconceptualize how you will introduce yourself to others to maximize effectiveness.

- Have topics of conversation in mind in case you get stuck or have trouble initiating conversations.

- Do not be afraid to approach people who are alone and engage in small talk.

- Be welcoming to others and try to be genuinely interested in what they have to say.

- Be approachable and personable.

# Self-Care

Interns and employees often find that balancing multiple aspects of their personal and professional lives simultaneously can be challenging. Intentional self-care can be crucial to navigating such demands successfully. Good eating, exercise, sleeping, time management, and work–life balance habits are always important. Some healthcare professionals experience burnout. To facilitate proper management, symptom recognition may be useful; diminished empathy, cynicism, physical exhaustion, sleep disturbances, lack of satisfaction from achievements, and emotional distancing from clients and colleagues have all been associated with burnout (Baird, 2008; Burnett & Evans, 2020). If you begin to experience such symptoms, take a step back and evaluate how you might improve balance and your well-being moving forward. Dixon's (2020) work with hospital and health system chief executive officers (CEOs) revealed the following considerations related to work–life balance:

- Decide what kind of life you want to live.

- Disconnect periodically and focus on you.

- Understand your limits. Journaling may help with this. If you begin to feel burned out, keep track of events that may be exacerbating your symptoms.

# Seeking a Job

Finding the right job requires self-awareness, planning, preparation, and diligence. Upon completion of your experiential learning, you should reflect on your occupational aspirations and intrinsic motivations. Recall which aspects of the experience interested and motivated you the most. This might help you identify a starting point for job searches. Remember, your mentors can be helpful with this as well. During your internship, you may see a job posting you would like to apply for. If this happens, discuss the opportunity with your site coordinator.

When evaluating potential places of employment, you may consider some of the same factors you considered when entertaining internship sites, such as geographic location and flexible scheduling. It is important to keep your future in mind. If you aspire to advance your career, be sure to consider whether organizations offer support for development and advancement, such as tuition assistance programs and leadership development programs. Ledlow and Stephens (2018) suggest that the average worker will change jobs up to nine times over the course of his or her career. Keep this in mind as a motivator to remain a resilient, lifelong learner.

As mentioned previously, the Handshake platform can help applicants find opportunities personalized for them. Students who intern in a hospital setting often forget the magnitude of healthcare facilities that exist. Remember to consider alternate settings as well. These include outpatient facilities, private practices, home health agencies, community health agencies, mental health centers, public health organizations, long term care facilities, imaging centers, and more (Makely, Austin, & Kester, 2017). In addition to Handshake, the internet offers vast resources that connect employers with potential employees, as do career fairs! Some sites even offer online résumé posting for potential consideration by employers (Makely, Austin, & Kester, 2017). A list of job-seeking websites is presented at the end of this chapter. Lastly, understand that many healthcare employers manage their own, individualized websites for job postings. If you need help navigating an organization's website, you can usually request assistance from its human resources department. Remember to draw upon all the tips discussed in this handbook related to professionalism as you prepare to enter the workforce! Also remember to congratulate yourself and safely celebrate your accomplishments!

## Personal Mission, Vision, and Values

In their book *Management Lessons from Mayo Clinic: Inside One of the World's Most Admired Service Organizations*, Berry and Seltman (2008, p. 154) assert the following about healthcare professionals: "The essential element underlying the unique, personal services performed is the value set from which the spontaneous service flows; kindness and humanely sensitive acts come more reliably from underlying values than from training sessions." As you consider employment opportunities (or perhaps even before—this may be a helpful exercise as you are writing your résumé), you may find it useful to conceptualize your personal and/or professional values and vision and mission statements (or update them if you have already done so). Li, Frohna, and Bostwick (2017) reinforce a clear connection between core value identification and career planning. Refer to Appendix B for a quick, five-step template to guide your value, vision, and mission statement development process. It is essential to understand that these dynamics can change and should be revisited and revised frequently. College Code, a provider of coaching and consultative services, offers great references for visual learners, including career map and LinkedIn profile checklist templates. Check them out here: https://www.mycollegecode.com/earlycareerpro.

## Healthcare Trends

As you enter the healthcare workforce, it is wise to be versed in some of the most common industry trends. This general information about the industry you are entering can be valuable, and you may find common knowledge of such issues useful during your interviews. Need a paper or project idea for internship? These would make great topics! While trends can vary depending on healthcare sector and other factors, this section is intended to present a brief list of a few hot topics from a leadership perspective. In the interest of brevity, the authors limited the following list to five items.

- Value-based healthcare: Literature contends that value-based payment structures that reward providers for quality care rather than quantity of care can lead to better patient outcomes, reduced costs, enhanced responsiveness to consumers, and better health for populations (CMS, 2020; Morrison, 2018). Healthcare leaders are faced with decisions on how to effectively transition their organizations to these new models of payment.

- Disruptive innovation: As out-of-industry companies such as Amazon, Google, Apple, and Walmart exert a greater presence in the healthcare field, more traditional hospitals, health systems, and providers will be challenged to adapt. Martin (2020) contends that providers must be able to provide high-quality digital patient experiences.

- Resiliency: Research suggests that resilient individuals exhibit several of the characteristics discussed in this handbook: self-awareness, self-motivation, and strong communication and problem-solving skills (AUPHA, 2020). Gokenbach (2017) explains how resilience facilitates change management and the ability to improvise. Paulus (2020) defines resilient healthcare workplaces as those that keep team members safe, reduce burnout, increase physician and employee satisfaction, and enhance patient experiences.

- Medical and technological advances: Healthcare innovations such as artificial intelligence (AI), genomic and precision medicine, and telehealth and virtual care are emerging rapidly (Kraft, 2020). Telehealth services are linked to the concept of value-based healthcare as they provide a means of expanding access. Organizations will be tasked with remaining abreast of these advances and evaluating and optimizing their utility.

- Strategic partnerships: Literature suggests that healthcare entities of the future may engage in nontraditional partnerships to better position themselves to adapt to the trends discussed above. Partners may include technology firms, retailers, and local public health entities (Saunders, 2020).

# Final Thoughts

Change is inevitable. To successfully navigate change and optimize your personal and professional journey, be sure to embrace lifelong learning, self-awareness, reflection, introspection, and growth. Join professional organizations, read professional publications, volunteer, seek and foster meaningful relationships, welcome feedback, identify what intrinsically motivates you, and perhaps most importantly, be deliberate about maintaining balance among these. Derived from Sweitzer and King's (2014) conceptualization of the engaged intern and Harris' (2016) principles of empowerment, Figure 7.1 is the authors' depiction of the factors that can influence your empowerment and success as an intern. Its purpose is to visually and simultaneously reinforce multiple concepts addressed in this handbook. Success is personal; use these constructs and the resources provided in Appendix C to further enhance your individualized development path. Do not be afraid to take risks occasionally, expand your comfort zone, and be deliberate about owning and learning from your mistakes. Be confident about the skills and knowledge you have acquired during your didactic and experiential learning opportunities, continue to refine and perfect them, and know how to articulate your competitive edge. Make a resounding impact. Good luck!

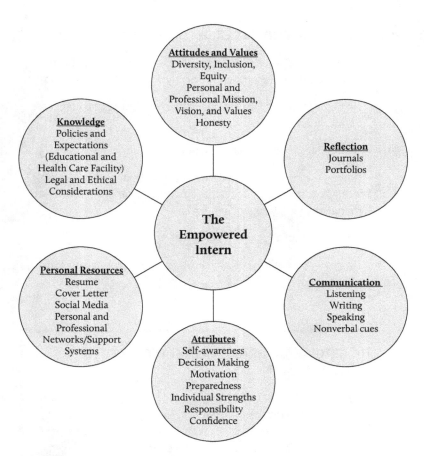

**FIGURE 7.1**    The Empowered Intern: Influencing Factors

Adapted from H. Frederick Sweitzer and Mary A. King, *The Successful Internship: Personal, Professional, and Civic Development in Experiential Learning*, p. 100. Copyright © 2014 by Cengage Learning, Inc.

## CONCLUDING THE INTERNSHIP REMINDERS

- Remember to reflect on your internship experience. Contemplate how these reflections inform your career aspirations.

- Remember to thank the people who contributed to the success of your internship experience.

- Be deliberate about building your professional network.

- Review all the tips covered in this work about résumé writing, interviewing, and professionalism as you prepare to find a job that aligns with your career goals.

- Be intentional about practicing self-care.

- Be ready to make your mark on the ever-important world of healthcare!

## EXERCISE/JOURNAL PROMPT: REFLECTION

Ernest Hemingway is commonly credited with authoring the six-word story, "For sale: baby shoes, never worn" (Smith, 2015, p. vi). Six-word stories can be fun and powerful exercises in brevity and reflection. Try your hand at creating a six-word story that is reflective of your experience as an intern. If you are feeling excessively inspired, create several!

## EXERCISE/JOURNAL PROMPT: CULTURAL PROFILES—BRINGING MULTIPLE CHAPTER CONCEPTS TOGETHER

Author Geri-Ann Galanti (2008) offers cultural profiles to assist healthcare professionals in caring for patients from diverging cultures. She gives an example of how Asian patients may be hesitant to or refrain from expressing their levels of pain. Reflect on how this knowledge accentuates what you have read about communication, bedside manner, diversity, and cultural competence.

Organize your thoughts on the Chapter 7 Journal Page provided or discuss in small groups (or both). Try to write at least 100 words.

## RESOURCES: JOB-SEEKING WEBSITES

Looking for a job? Have you tried these sites?

- www.careerbuilder.com/Jobs
- www.glassdoor.com
- www.healthcarejobsite.com
- www.hospitalcareers.com
- www.indeed.com
- www.monster.com
- https://publichealthjobs.org
- www.ziprecruiter.com

Some sites specialize in recruiting people for specific occupations, such as nursing. Here is an example:

- www.nurse.com/jobs

# Chapter 7 Journal Page

# References

Association of University Programs in Health Administration (AUPHA) and Studer Community Institute. (2020). *Resilience and well-being in stressful times: A tool kit for health administration educators.* https:// higherlogicdownload.s3.amazonaws.com/AUPHA/5c0a0c07-a7f7-413e-ad73-9b7133ca4c38/UploadedImages/Publications/ AUPHA_WELLNESS_TOOL_KIT__10-08-20_.pdf

Baird, B. N. (2008). *The internship, practicum, and field placement handbook: A guide for the helping professions* (5th ed.). Upper Saddle River, NJ: Pearson/Prentice Hall.

Berry, L. L., & Seltman, K. D. (2008). *Management lessons from Mayo Clinic: Inside one of the world's most admired service organizations.* New York, NY: McGraw-Hill.

Burnett, B. & Evans, D. (2020). *Designing your work life: How to thrive and change and find happiness at work.* New York, NY: Alfred A. Knopf.

Centers for Medicare & Medicaid Services (CMS). (2020). *What are the value-based programs?* https://www.cms.gov/Medicare/Quality-Initiatives-Patient-Assessment-Instruments/Value-Based-Programs/ Value-Based-Programs

Dixon, D. L. (2020). *Diversity on the executive path: Wisdom and insights for navigating to the highest levels of healthcare leadership.* Chicago, IL: Health Administration Press.

Frisina, M. (2014). *Influential leadership: Change your behavior, change your organization, change health care.* Chicago, IL: Health Administration Press.

Galanti, G. (2008). *Caring for patients from different cultures: Case studies from American hospitals.* Philadelphia, PA: University of Pennsylvania Press.

Ghaye, T., & Lillyman, S. (2010). *Reflection: Principles and practices for healthcare professionals* (2nd ed.). London, Eng.: Quay Books.

Gokenbach, V. (2017). *Phoenix leadership: The healthcare executive's strategy for relevance and resilience.* Boca Raton, FL: CRC Press. https:// doi.org/10.1201/b21818

Goleman, D. (2005). *Emotional intelligence: Why it can matter more than IQ.* New York, NY: Bantam Dell.

Harris, R. B. (2016). *Empowerment: Cross-cultural perspectives, strategies and psychological benefits.* Nova Science Publishers, Inc.

Johns, M. L. (2017). *Leadership development for healthcare: A pathway, process, and workbook.* Chicago, IL: American Health Information Management Association.

Kraft, D. (2020). Technologies that are shaping the future of health and medicine. In *Future scan 2020–2025: Health care trends and implications* (pp. 26–30). Chicago, IL: American Hospital Association.

Ledlow, G. R., & Stephens, J. H. (2018). *Leadership for health professionals: Theory, skills, and applications.* Burlington, MA: Jones and Bartlett Learning.

Li, S., Frohna, J., & Bostwick, S. (2017). Using your personal mission statement to INSPIRE and achieve success. *Academic Pediatrics, 17*(2), 107–109. https://doi.org/10.1016/j.acap.2016.11.010

Makely, S., Austin, V. J., & Kester, Q. (2017). *Professionalism in health care: A primer for career success* (5th ed.). Upper Saddle River, NJ: Pearson Education.

Martin, A. (2020). Disruptive innovation: The impact of new entrants on the future of health care. In *Future scan 2020–2025: Health care trends and implications* (pp. 5–9). Chicago, IL: American Hospital Association.

Morrison, I. (2018). Moving ahead on the long road toward value-based healthcare. In *Future scan 2018–2023: Healthcare trends and implications* (p. 2). Chicago, IL: American Hospital Association.

National Association of Colleges and Employers (NACE). (2020). *15 best practices for internship programs.* https://www.naceweb.org/talent-acquisition/internships/15-best-practices-for-internship-programs/

Paulus, R. A. (2020). Building a resilient health care organization. In *Future scan 2020–2025: Health care trends and implications* (pp. 21–25). Chicago, IL: American Hospital Association.

Pink, D. H. (2009). *Drive: The surprising truth about what motivates us.* New York, NY: Riverhead Books.

RoAne, S. (2016). *How to work a room and other secrets of savvy networking.* Society for Human Resource Management (SHRM). https://www.shrm.org/resourcesandtools/hr-topics/organizational-and-employee-development/pages/viewpoint-how-to-work-a-room-susan-roane.aspx

Saunders, N. M. (2020). Disruptive innovation: The impact of new entrants on the future of health care. In *Future scan 2020–2025: Health care trends and implications* (pp. 15–20). Chicago, IL: American Hospital Association.

Smith, L. (Ed.). (2015). *The best advice in six words: Writers famous and obscure on love, sex, money, friendship, family, work, and much more.* New York, NY: St. Martin's Griffin.

Sweitzer, H. F., & King, M. A. (2014). *The successful internship: Personal, professional, and civic development in experiential learning.* Boston, MA: Cengage Learning.

Thistlethwaite, J., & McKimm, J. (2016). *Health care professionalism at a glance.* West Sussex, Eng.: Wiley Blackwell.

# 8

# INTERNSHIP STORIES

## Overview

Both authors of this handbook have been faculty mentors and internship coordinators for an undergraduate healthcare systems administration program. They have witnessed and interacted with students who had extremely successful internships that led to professional jobs in the student's area of study. Unfortunately, they have also worked with students who did not communicate well, behave in a professional manner, or listen to the advice of the internship coordinator. In chapter 8, the authors are excited to share six stories inspired by interns from their organization. The last three internship accounts are from students. Enjoy!

## Intern A—Faculty Perspective

Intern A communicated with the internship coordinator on a regular basis prior to his internship. Most interns in Intern A's program complete their internship as the last course(s) in the program. Intern A was a student athlete and could not follow this traditional curriculum. He was proactive in asking for advice in the planning of his internship. He was able to secure an intern position in a major healthcare system in the areas of quality and risk management. He was professional, asked appropriate questions, and worked hard every day. He was not afraid to take on projects and always completed them to the best of his abilities and demonstrated good follow-through. He did his projects and communicated with his faculty mentor about the progress of his internship.

The site coordinator called the faculty coordinator and asked if they could pay the intern even though the initial posting was that of an unpaid internship. The site coordinator said he was doing the work of an employee; he was professional and deserved to be compensated. Of course, the faculty coordinator agreed. At the conclusion of his internship, he was offered a full-time position with this major healthcare organization. The intern needed to return to campus to complete his final classes and compete in his last season of athletics. The major healthcare organization held the job for him for an entire semester. This likely would not have happened if he had been an average intern. He showed his value to the organization and it recognized and rewarded him.

Attributes observed by faculty: positive attitude, excellent written and oral communication skills, willingness to take risks, and good listening and time management skills.

## Intern C—Faculty Perspective

Intern C was an average student. He was not overly motivated but came to class and did enough to get by. Intern C played on a club sport team at the university and was quite often tired when he came to class. Intern C had never held a job because he was active in sports and did not need the money while he was a student. When it was time to secure an internship, he asked to meet with the faculty coordinator. He explained that his brother was going to school at a university in another state and he wanted to do his internship there. The faculty coordinator asked him if he planned to work there at the conclusion of his internship. He responded, "No, I'm going to move back home to find a job but wanted the experience of living in another state." The faculty coordinator asked the student to consider the advantages of completing an internship at a place he wanted to seek future employment. She described the importance of networking and building a résumé. He appreciated the input but asked to do his internship as requested. The faculty coordinator agreed but told him it may not be in his best interest. He found an internship site and completed his internship out of state. Upon graduation, he was not able to find a job. He applied for many positions, but his résumé lacked substance. He asked to meet with the faculty coordinator a year after graduation to obtain advice on searching for a job. During the meeting, Intern C revealed he felt he made a few mistakes in his life; one was not securing basic employment experience and the other was doing his internship out of state. He realized that his networking was limited and the lack of depth on his résumé was limiting his employment options. He was applying for positions above his skill and experience level.

Attributes observed by faculty: pleasant personality, a tendency for laziness, and lack of ambition. Although he wanted to find work, he was not willing to work his way up in an organization.

# Intern F—Faculty Perspective

Intern F found an internship position with a major healthcare organization. He was able to secure an intern position in human resources. He was an average student who was given a fabulous opportunity to learn and grow. In the third week of his internship, the faculty coordinator received a phone call from the site saying they sent him home and he was no longer welcome at their organization. When the faculty coordinator asked what happened, this is what she was told: he expressed no interest in learning, he was lazy and defensive, and he thought he knew more than the people working in the department. However, she went on to explain that there was a specific incident that took place that day. She invited the intern to a meeting with the executive team—the chief executive officer (CEO), chief financial officer (CFO), vice president of human resources, and chief nursing officer (CNO)—and thought he would be able to network and learn about the organization. The CFO was giving a presentation and the intern leaned his head against the wall, stretched his legs out in front of him, and showed a lack of interest and respect for the people in the meeting. After his presentation was complete, the CFO told the VP of HR that he wanted the disrespectful intern out of their organization today. The faculty coordinator was very embarrassed for the student and how his performance reflected negatively on the program. She scheduled a meeting with the intern, and he told her that the meeting was boring. She explained how this incident could impact his future. He was not allowed to go back to the site, and he was placed in the hiring system as not eligible for employment. This means he was not employable with their hospitals and other entities throughout the United States.

The student had to find another internship site that was willing to take him to complete his internship. He ended up going to a six-bed, assisted nursing facility. His experience there paled to what it would have been at the major healthcare facility.

Attributes observed by faculty: no self-accountability, poor attitude, lack of respect for others, and lack of ambition.

# Intern 1—Student Perspective

It is true that there are no dumb questions, rather limitless opportunities to ask questions of subject matter experts who feel their answers are obvious or a common truth learned from years of experiences and observations. It is also true that mastery of skill is not obtained instantaneously but through endless amounts of experimentation, observation, humility, and perseverance. At its core, the internship gives someone who knows just enough to be dangerous the opportunity to observe, ask questions of people who have spent years or even a lifetime crafting their skill, take risks on a small-scale and learn from the outcomes, be embarrassed, be proud, be vulnerable, and figure out what's next?

A line from season one of the popular show Grey's Anatomy is a true reflection of what it is like to be fresh out of school with nothing but sheer excitement and terror. In this episode, an eager and terrified medical intern sits in a hallway with his fellow interns after their first day on the job and states "who here feels like they have no idea what they are doing?" This sentiment, whether you are a medical intern or a business school intern, perfectly captures what it is like to go from school simulations and principle teachings to real-world issues with real people at the end of your decisions. It. Is. Terrifying. The good news? The internship, provided you pick one that will challenge you and encourage growth, will allow you to "fail small" and learn more than you could have ever imagined. Given the opportunity to take on an internship in a hometown, working for someone you or your parents know may not give you the chance to be bold and truly extend beyond your comfort zone. Aligning oneself with people who will challenge and push you is paramount and the only way to get the most out of this limited experience.

Many students underestimate the power of an internship, viewing it as a check in the box and a means to an end. Do yourself a favor and do not subscribe to that school of thought. An internship for you is an opportunity to learn about things beyond the classroom and learn about yourself as you transition from a life of a full-time student to the life of a full-time employee. The worlds are very different. What is the value of interning with a great organization? The organization considers it a long interview and they are constantly looking at how you present yourself and your work. They care how you advocate for yourself and for others. They care that you put effort into something even if you missed the mark. Do not take this opportunity for granted. Pick a site that will challenge you, push you, support you, and set you up for opportunities at the end even if that ends up being somewhere else.

I left Ferris State University as a shy 21-year-old who had lived in the Upper Peninsula her whole life and then went out on a limb and moved to Big Rapids for college. For context, Big Rapids felt like a huge place at the time. I decided to take an unpaid internship in Ann Arbor, MI at a highly complex healthcare system over 8 hours away from any friends or family. I volunteered for things, I showed up to meetings, I added value where I thought I could, I respected and listened to experts, I got to know people, and I remembered stories they told me and thanked them for their time. It has been 10 years since I first stepped foot on the campus of that healthcare system and I continue to show up for work at that same organization today because of the work I put in during my internship. This experience matters. Make it count!

# Intern 2—Student Perspective

The experiences and connections gained from my internship were critical in helping the success of my career after graduating Ferris State University. The content taught by the staff at Ferris was relevant and in alignment with many of the current trends in health care administration today. By completing projects in key areas throughout operations within a health system I was able to understand aspects of many support services that I was not as familiar with. Through these interviews I also was introduced many senior level leaders who were able to share with me their experiences, pathways, and advice. Hearing firsthand the unique ways these leaders crafted their careers way eye opening and demonstrated there is no "textbook" way into hospital administration. I also was able to see the passion and engagement that many of these individuals had in their profession and it was evident that they found a great amount of fulfilment in their work. After completing my degree, I was lucky enough to find employment within this same organization. The connections I had made during my internship were what helped me climb into my leadership position and experiencing a level of success.

# Intern 3—Student Perspective

My experience with the alternative internship was great. It was, however, a lot of work. Doing the internship online gave me some advantages that doing a regular internship would not have. For instance, I was able to get more in-depth with the assignments that I was doing. This gave me the opportunity to learn more about the projects that I had chosen to do.

We were given a total of five book reviews to complete for the 16 weeks. At first look, I thought that this many book reviews was going to be impossible to do along with all the other work that was given. After reading the first one I was very excited to do the others. I read books that I would not have normally read and gained a greater understanding of how certain things in the healthcare field work. I was able to finish both classes early. I was done in mid-October.

The only downfall to doing my internship this way was now that I'm done with school and applying to get a job and start my career, I'm worried no one wants to hire me because I don't have any experience in the field. This is so important, even if it's just the experience from the internship. I am now looking into going on and getting my master's degree. Hopefully by the time I'm finished the world will be back to normal. I was very fortunate to have great professors all the way through my schooling and had the honor of working with a great advisor during my online internship. I feel very fortunate to have found a great university to go to.

## EXERCISE/JOURNAL PROMPT: REFLECTION ON INTERNS A, C, AND F

After reviewing the first three internship stories, what are your impressions? Are there attributes displayed by these individuals that you aspire to? Are there attributes displayed by these individuals that you think could have been improved upon? If you were offering advice to these individuals, how would you advise them to proceed with their transition to the healthcare workplace?

Organize your thoughts on the Chapter 8 Journal Page provided or discuss in small groups (or both). Try to write at least 200 words.

## EXERCISE/JOURNAL PROMPT: REFLECTION ON INTERN C

Consider the following points:

- Research suggests that employers utilize internship programs to feed their hiring pipelines (Allen, 2013), and a major factor influencing hiring decisions is the quality of the intern's performance at the site (Saltikoff, 2017).

- A case could also be made about the quality of an internship experience regardless of location.

Considering these points and Intern C's story, reflect on how Intern C could have better optimized his experiential learning opportunity.

Organize your thoughts on the Chapter 8 Journal Page provided or discuss in small groups (or both). Try to write at least 100 words.

# Chapter 8 Journal Page

# References

Allen, C. (2013). *Key strategies for converting interns.* National Association of Colleges and Employers. https://www.naceweb.org/talent-acquisition/internships/key-strategies-for-converting-interns/

Saltikoff, N. (2017). *The positive implications of internships on early career outcomes.* National Association of Colleges and Employers. https://www.naceweb.org/job-market/internships/the-positive-implications-of-internships-on-early-career-outcomes/

# Appendix A

## *Sample Résumé and Cover Letter*

## **Jane Doe**
(888) 777-6666 • jdoe@sample.com

**Summary Statement:**
Seeking an internship that complements and advances my knowledge, creativity, leadership, organizational, and communication skills. Dual majors in healthcare systems administration and radiography have provided me with synergistic clinical and supervisory skills that I am eager to apply in an acute care hospital setting.

**Highlights:**

- 3 years of experience training and leading others

- 3 years of experience planning events and activities

- Experience creating and editing employee material

- Extensive experience with Microsoft Office

**Education**:
SAMPLE UNIVERSITY, Big Rapids, MI

- Bachelor of Science in Healthcare Systems
  Administration                                     05/2020

- Associate Degree in Radiography               05/2020

- Cumulative GPA: 3.6

SAMPLE HIGH SCHOOL, San Francisco, CA

- GPA: 4.0                                                05/2015

**Licenses & Certifications**:
Basic Life Support for Healthcare Providers (BLS)   06/2019–06/2021

- Credential ID: ABCD1EF

**Occupational Experience**:
Sample University Cafeteria, Big Rapids, MI         03/2018–present

**Secretary**

- Created two Canvas training courses and managed the training of 30 student employees

- Edited and created new hire material

- Managed all disciplinary write-ups and other paperwork

- Hired, scheduled, trained, and gave tours of the facility for new student employees

- Approved and edited student employee shifts for payroll, entered data into Excel, and created basic Access databases

**Volunteer Experience**:
**Vice President of Community Service**
National Society of Collegiate Scholars        04/2019—present

- Created, facilitated, and marketed volunteer and fundraiser activities

- Collaborated with nonprofit organizations to provide volunteer opportunities

- Managed volunteers and the local Collegiate Scholars social media page

- Conceptualized professional development and leadership opportunities for students

**References**:
**John Doe, Manager**
Sample University Cafeteria
999 Campus Drive
Big Rapids, MI 49307
222-333-4444
manager@sampleuniversity.edu

**Sample Name, Associate Professor, Health Administration Program, Sample University**
Sample University
888 Campus Drive
Big Rapids, MI 49307
555-666-7777
professor@sampleuniversity.edu

# Jane Doe
(888) 777-6666 • jdoe@sample.com

January 8, 2021

Mr. Very Caring
Sample Acute Care Hospital
1111 Hospital Drive
Sample City, MI 22222

Dear Mr. Caring,

After researching multiple potential internship locations, I believe I can best grow and learn from professionals within Sample Acute Care Hospital. I strongly identify with your commitment to providing quality, technologically advanced care to diverse populations of clients in your surrounding communities.

I am a dedicated, hardworking, creative, organized individual who is passionate about healthcare. My work and volunteer experience at Sample University has sharpened my ability to train individuals, plan events, and communicate and collaborate via writing and social media platforms.

I would love to discuss my qualifications in person and have a chance to interview for the available administrative internship position. I am passionate about serving future patients and helping others. Thank you kindly for the consideration.

Respectfully,

Jane Doe

# Appendix B

## *Mission, Vision, Values Template*

*Adapted from Li, Frohna, and Bostwick (2017) and Johns (2017)*

**Step 1**: Identify your core values. These values will be inherent to you and will remain consistent regardless of circumstances, setting, or activity (Li, Frohna, & Bostwick, 2016). To help identify your core values, Li, Frohna, and Bostwick (2017) suggest considering constructs such as accomplishments you are proud of and qualities you admire in yourself and your role models. Examples of core values may include integrity, diversity, honesty, and lifelong learning. Note: this is a great exercise in reflection!

List your core values here:


**Step 2**: Formulate your professional vision. When you think about your vision, think future. Li, Frohna, and Bostwick (2017, p. 108) assert that your vision is what "the world will look like after you have accomplished the changes you want to make." Example: A health administration student's vision may be to oversee the leading healthcare organization in the nation.

Write your vision statement here:


**Step 3**: Develop your professional mission statement. This statement should convey your actions to fulfill your purpose. Example: A health administration student's mission statement may be to commit to improving the health of a specified population through collaborative, honest leadership within an acute care setting.

Draft your mission statement here:

**Step 4**: Identify the following to align with your mission:

- Activities to be completed—these may become professional goals

- Skills to be obtained—these may also become professional goals. Goals should be specific, achievable, and time-bound (define a date by which you would like to achieve the goal). Johns (2017) attests that goal attainment requires commitment, self-regulation, and monitoring of progress.

- People who can help you

Identify those items here:

**Step 5**: Remember to review and revise your mission, vision, and values regularly!

# References

Johns, M. L. (2017). *Leadership development for healthcare: A pathway, process, and workbook*. Chicago, IL: American Health Information Management Association.

Li, S., Frohna, J., & Bostwick, S. (2017). Using your personal mission statement to INSPIRE and achieve success. *Academic Pediatrics*, 17(2), 107–109. https://doi.org/10.1016/j.acap.2016.11.010

# Appendix C

## *Recommended Resources/ Self-Assessment Tools*

The American College of Healthcare Executives (ACHE, 2020) presents multiple self-assessment tools such as those evaluating change management, conflict management, emotional intelligence, leadership, and work-life balance. Additional suggestions include ACHE's interview prep and résumé review tools.

Burnett and Evans (2020) present simple ideas for designing and reframing your work life, such as a checklist to gauge one's ability to create meaningful work.

Although an older resource, Chambers (2000) offers several impactful communication self-evaluation tools, including personal assessments on giving and receiving criticism.

Dixon (2020) shares real-life experiences and career advancement stories of twelve racially and ethnically diverse healthcare administrators. Students may identify with interviewed individuals and seek inspiration from their experiences.

Dye (2017) features tools for evaluating the leader, the team, and the self. This resource may be of particular interest to students currently holding or aspiring to attain leadership positions within healthcare.

The Enneagram Institute (2019) markets the Riso-Hudson Enneagram Type Indicator (RHETI), a personality test designed to contribute to your understanding of self and others.

Johns (2017) offers exercises and activities related to personal strengths, values, mindfulness, ethical practice, and more.

If you are looking for personal finance tips during an internship, Knox (2016) offers suggestions on topics such as spending, checking accounts, loans, building credit, and investment basics.

Malvey and Sapp (2020) offer a digital self-evaluation assessment tool. Each assessment item, such as adaptability, creativity, and maturity, are mapped to goals and recommended actions to not only achieve such goals but to also ensure they are evident in your online presence.

The Myers-Briggs Company (2020) offers the Myers-Briggs Type Indicator (MBTI) as a means of measuring psychological personality preferences. This tool can be very useful not only in your journey of self-discovery but also to your understanding of others.

The National Association of Colleges and Employers (NACE, 2020) shares career readiness resources such as the Professional Competency Self-Assessment Tool.

The National Association of Colleges and Employers offers resources to students who identify as lesbian, gay, bisexual, transgender, or queer (LGBTQ), including the level of employment nondiscrimination protection provided by individual states (Greathouse, 2019).

The National Association of Colleges and Employers also highlights literature surrounding populations such as students with autism, disabilities, and first-generation students (NACE, 2021).

Tipton (2017) offers a personality self-assessment that allows readers to reflect on their agreeableness, extroversion, neuroticism, openness to experience, conscientiousness, and other dimensions.

The University of Pittsburgh's Graduate School of Public Health (2020) offers a job-search toolkit with advice pertaining to writing cover letters, preparing for interviews, negotiating salaries, and more.

The VIA Institute on Character (2020) offers a free character strengths survey.

# References

American College of Healthcare Executives (ACHE). (2020). *Products and services*. https://www.ache.org/career-resource-center/products-and-services

Burnett, B. & Evans, D. (2020). *Designing your work life: How to thrive and change and find happiness at work*. New York, NY: Alfred A Knopf.

Chambers, H. E. (2000). *Effective communication skills for scientific and technical professionals*. Cambridge, MA: Perseus.

Dixon, D. L. (2020). *Diversity on the executive path: Wisdom and insights for navigating to the highest levels of healthcare leadership*. Chicago, IL: Health Administration Press.

Dye, C. F. (2017). *Leadership in healthcare: Essential values and skills*. Chicago, IL: Health Administration Press.

Enneagram Institute. (2019). *The Riso-Hudson Enneagram Type Indicator (RHETI version 2.5)*. https://www.enneagraminstitute.com/rheti

Greathouse, M. (2019). *Career considerations of LGBTQ students*. https://www.naceweb.org/career-development/special-populations/career-considerations-of-lgbtq-students/

Johns, M. L. (2017). *Leadership development for healthcare: A pathway, process, and workbook*. Chicago, IL: American Health Information Management Association.

Knox, S. (2016). *Financial basics: A money-management guide for students* (2nd ed.). Columbus: Ohio State University Press.

Malvey, D., & Sapp, J. (2020). *Your healthcare job hunt: How your digital presence can make or break your career*. Chicago, IL: Health Administration Press.

Myers-Briggs Company. (2020). *Build a foundation for personal growth*. https://www.mbtionline.com/en-US/Products/For-you

National Association of Colleges and Employers. (2020). *Career readiness resources: Sample assessments*. https://www.naceweb.org/career-readiness/competencies/sample-assessments/

National Association of Colleges and Employers. (2021). *Special populations*. https://www.naceweb.org/career-development/special-populations/

Tipton, D. (2017). *Personal and professional growth for health care professionals*. Burlington, MA: Jones and Bartlett Learning.

University of Pittsburgh Graduate School of Public Health (2020). *Job search tool kit.* https://www.publichealth.pitt.edu/careers/job-search-tool-kit

VIA Institute on Character. (2020). *The VIA character strengths survey.* https://www.viacharacter.org/survey/account/register